The Immo

MW00619874

Becoming A Creative Human Being versus Developing A Criminal Personality

Dr. Jerome L. Schulte M.D.

To

Renee'

Thanks for being a part of the evening

Enjoy

Jerome L Schulte md

May 1, 2013

The Immortality Complex:

Becoming A Creative Human Being versus Developing A Criminal Personality

Dr. Jerome L. Schulte M.D.

ISBN: 978-0-9883568-1-8
Library of Congress Control Number: 2012917308

Published by Inkwell Productions
10869 N. Scottsdale Road # 103-128
Scottsdale, AZ 85254-5280

Tel. 480-315-3781
E-mail info@inkwellproductions.com
Website www.inkwellproductions.com

Printed in the United States of America

ENDORSEMENTS

Many years ago, I found myself baffled regarding how to understand and treat a psychotic individual who murdered another. I strongly believed that it was a matter of time and persistence before I would find someone who developed an approach to understand and treat this condition. Through my research, I located a tape of Treating the Psychotic Homicidal Offender by Dr. Jerome Schulte. The perspective advocated by the tape appeared to be straightforward but yet powerful in being able to understand and then treat these most fragile psychiatric patients. I tried to locate Dr. Schulte for supervision but was unable to. Of particular note, at the time, I was in the process of completing a forensic evaluation of an adult who committed a matricide. Once finished, I believed that the evaluation was comprehensive, and defendable in court. However, after learning of Dr. Schulte's approach, I started to evaluate the person from the standpoint of reconstructive therapy, and saw a different humanistic-forensic profile. The person who I initially believed to be not dangerous, I now viewed as dangerous and in need of continued secure hospitalization. Subsequently, despite a lengthy period of clinical stability, he started to assault staff. At the time, I was astonished how Dr. Schulte's model so clearly provided me with a perspective that was so applicable, but yet so unknown.

Since I was so astonished at how effective the model had been, I persisted in my search. It took me two years to located Dr. Schulte since he had retired from Atascadero Forensic Hospital. He was gracious to speak to me regarding contacting him for supervision despite being at humanitarian fund raiser at the time. I believe that I was very fortunate to both be able to more fully learn his model but to get to know the kind and deeply insightful person, who took time out to speak to me in this rather awkward situation. Since that time, Dr. Schulte and I have been in contact for five years and I have found, just like he has advocated, that his approach can be effective with one's own personal and spiritual development as well as applicable to variety of clinical and forensic problems.

I have found Dr. Schulte's therapeutic perspective to be vital in helping people grow and mature. In addition, his model also has great clinical and forensic utility by being able to explain how and why individuals use more deviant and criminal behaviors to negotiate the same stages, of human development, and dysfunctional manner. This perspective of focusing on how the person tried to attain similar developmental growth, and the disorder, or offensive lifestyle. Dr. Schulte's perspective is comprehensive yet with a variety of persons including children, adolescents and adults. The significance of his profound perspective is that it is highly heuristic in that one framework applies both for human growth as well as where the criminal personality deviates. The insights in this book will inform both anyone interested in the essentials of personal and spiritual development, and be a standard text for future clinicians for generations to come. It is with deep felt honor that I have come to know Dr. Schulte and now be able to advocate for a more widespread dissemination of his ideas. I highly recommend this groundbreaking book.

Lino Faccini, Ph.d.

The first time the "humanness" theory was introduced to me in adjudication, I was quite perplexed. I had trouble figuring out what the meaning behind it all was. After studying the subject matter more in depth, your ideas and comcepts are astonishing. It takes a mature person to sit and truly contemplate the meaning behind the affectual and physical universe and the criminal personality. After two semesters of reading and discussing the different feelings and content that goes with each feeling has definitely been an enlightening experience to understanding people. As a forensic phychiatrist you have gotten to the root of a person's essence, and as a lawyer I hope to use these tools to understand people I work with; whether I am prosecuting them or defending them. The essence of a person is the origin in which their personality, actions and thoughts begin; so understanding it is crucial

Thank you for giving me this tool in order to understand criminals and the true humanniss of people collectively. Using two words, unchangeable and timelessness, as the definition of essence served as the basis for understanding and enabled me to grasp the ideas in a more immediate fashion.

Another topic that made so much sense in my mind was the theory of contradiction. "There is nothing that can exist in life with vital force that does not contain contradiction. It is a measure of that force that the contradiction can be grasped and endured(p.19)." Not only does contradiction serve a purpose, it creates an understanding of life; which is innate for me. I have a hard time putting my understanding into words, because I feel like it is so natural and that it just makes sense. It is almost an instinctive quality, it is hard to explain. When I read the material it flows so well and my mind perceives it and turns it into understanding in my brain. In other words I can not explain why it makes sense, it just does.

I thoroughly enjoyed reading this book and I look forward to referring back to it in order to understand people better down to the root of their essence.

Charise Weatherbee, *Grand Canyon University*

The whole purpose of "The Immortality Complex" is to understand the essence of humanness and give the reader a better sense of understanding about what it is that we all share as humans. Basic to the human growth process is recognizing that there is something intrinsic in the nature of humanness that is of value and the most crucial element of being human, present from the time of birth, is *need*. Dr. Schulte proposes that the driving force behind need, and consequently the essence of humanness are feelings, Feelings? As Dr. Schulte once pointed out in a lecture, when was the last time anybody ever took a class about feelings? I know I haven't. But first you feel, *then* you know.

Just as we must discover together what is inherent in all humans, we must face together inherent problems in our world society. Such problems include learning how to deal with the criminal personality. Section II of the book ties together the fact that all human beings are of value with the fact that all human beings have two sides to their personality. The dark side of our personality is just as inherent to our essence as humans as the bright side.

Perhaps Dr. Schulte's most profound statement regarding the criminal personality is that "this process of moving from a *personal identity* that is quite attuned to adjusting to an ongoing society, to a *universal identity*, is at present most difficult to accomplish while at the same time remaining adjusted to society at large."

On more than one occasion I paused while reading the book to ponder the complexity of being human. The complexity alone points to the absoluteness of a greater being. I was able to gain a better appreciation for the complexity and great beauty that lies within the essence of humanness, that lies within the essence of me.

Amanda Moncayo Parker, *Grand Canyon University, Georgetown School of Law Graduate May 2012*

My initial response to the content of your book was that of "what does this have to do with forensics or criminology?" All of the talk about energy, the universe and contradiction made me think I was reading a strict philosophy. It wasn't until later that I began to realize the scope of the book and the group that it attempted to diagnose: the effect that the universe *universally* has on the whole human race. As I began to understand the concepts of energy and vitality, it became apparent that this was a broad, all-encompassing philosophy volume that would diagnose criminology through its philosophy, validating its consistency as a philosophy.

My favorite aspect of your work was its attempt to explain the personal, psychological and emotional woes of people as a failure to or lack of sufficiently satisfying the intrinsic needs that we all have. When needs aren't met and a discrepancy between normal and criminal is made, people either search for a solution, find it, don't find it, act out in anguish, keep searching, or any combination of the preceding.

All in all, I enjoyed the reads from the book as stimulating and well conceived from years and countless hours of experience. It was an excellent insight into the universal scale of mental, physical and spiritual processes that we are all measured on.

Josh Skube, *Grand Canyon University*

Don't you believe
that there is in man
a deep so profound as
to be hidden even to
him in whom it is?

Saint Augustine

CONTENTS

Section Two: The Physical Universe:
A Study of the Criminal Personality

Section Three: A Spiritual Universe: The Creative Being

*This book is dedicated to my 6 children who have been my
inspiration throughout life. Sarah Jane Vandermark,
Jeremy Benjamin Schulte, Amanda Elizabeth McNulty,
Gretchen Mary Buckley, Michael Lewis Schulte
and Gregory Jerome Schulte.*

INTRODUCTION

To be human can be a joyful experience. To strive for an understanding, an appreciation and fulfillment of our humanness may seem to be an enormous task. Yet, that is why we are here in this world and why we, ceaselessly, feel internally driven to search for meaning in our lives. To become an active creative participant in the development of one's community, country, and newly emerging world society is a goal frequently desired by many people and the subject matter of this book.

Section I lays out a structured format for the development of the "affectual" or internal feeling side of our human personality. Section II opens doors to an understanding of the antisocial side of our humanness, which has been steadfastly avoided throughout the history of civilization. It is dramatically different than anything previously written anywhere about the essence of human beings. Section III outlines the steps to become a creative being.

Positive growth is used throughout the book as the core to further one's development, understanding, and fulfillment. Additionally, this book details remedies for human emotional problems and destructive criminal personalities that have plagued societies throughout history. These problems have taken a tremendous toll in short-circuiting humankind's ability for fulfillment and creativity.

I began writing this book more than forty years ago to assimilate my ever-expanding diverse clinical and administrative psychiatric experiences. As my experiences evolved, so has this book. It became the text for my classes in justice studies at Grand Canyon University. The text and its principles are now being successfully utilized through my reconstructive therapy as a basis for treatment in New York State by Lino Faccini, Ph.d. *American Journal of Forensic Psychiatry*, vol. 31, Issue 4, 2010, and "Is Developmentally Informed Therapy for Persons with ID and Criminal Personality/Offenses Relevant?" *Advances in Psychology Research*, vol. 71.

Two of my earlier papers, illustrate the processes that validate the reintegration and synthesis of a group of 46 subjects under the format explained in Sections One and Two. "Study and Treatment of 46 Psychotic Patients with Convictions of Homicide,"[4] and "Long-Term Treatment of a Psychotic Patient: A Case Study" *American Journal of Forensic Psychiatry,* vol. VIII, No. 3, 1987/47 and vol. IX, No. 3, 1988/59.[5]

Section Two also includes examples of work with very young children, manifesting evidence of moving toward a life of crime, whose outcome was able to be changed quickly and dramatically in a positive direction.

This book also provides a new perspective for individual and societal fulfillment based on 250,000 overall successful patient therapy hours. The multifaceted obsession with remaining youthful, with health, and a desire not to be forgotten or ignored by society and the universe is crystallized in the concept of "the immortality complex". Thus, the immortality complex is an integral part of each and every individual human being as well as society as a whole. This book therefore has applicability for people of all ages and walks of life. Societies, including the emerging world society, ideally would benefit from an understanding and implementation of its content into their educational systems.

Life's Guarantee

You have but one
and only one
guarantee in life:
that you will spend
every moment
with one person.

SECTION I

The Affectual Universe
First You Feel, Then You Know

Essence
is defined
by
timelessness
and
permanence.

Chapter 1
The Essence of Humanness

Synopsis:

Vulnerability is a universal experience shared by all human beings, based on some measure of deprivation.

All human beings are of value and hence the essence of humanness must be valuable. Essence is a function of the dimensions of permanence or sameness and the dimension of timelessness.

Need is found to meet those criteria of sameness, permanency, and timelessness in all human beings. The essence of humanness is ultimately defined as need. By definition, therefore, the value of humanness is a function of need. Performance, which has been the accepted standard and driving force throughout the history of civilization, is its contradiction.

One of the nearly universal observable characteristics of any human relationship is the vulnerability each person ultimately feels in one or more areas of his/her relationships.

The husband who becomes jealous or suspicious of his wife conversing with another man at a party might become enraged once they return home. His vulnerability to this situation *could* repeat itself for years. The wife reacts with equal intensity about the lack of trust she feels from her mate and her own vulnerability, although a bit more subtle, becomes evident and equally repetitive. This is just one of many examples. Another emotion commonly felt by both partners is a sense of not being appreciated. It might be the most universal vulnerability of all.

The question arises, What is the essence of vulnerability? What is the intrinsic fact that sets up the dynamic forces resulting in this feeling or state of vulnerability, which often wreak havoc with relationships that begin on such apparently blissful notes?

Very simply, I define vulnerability as something we need without which we feel empty or relatively deprived and vulnerable. The man in our example might say; "I need to have more of your time." The woman may say, "I need to feel you trust." As we progress to the heart of the matter, let us limit our discussion to her vulnerability. The dynamics in the man's vulnerability in this example are more complicated and we will reserve them for later.

I have found that if I question the woman closely about exactly what she means, when she talks of needing to be trusted, her reply will invariably involve the concept of being a good person. Trust ultimately leads to a feeling of the presence of goodness or value. I have questioned hundreds of people about what they feel is the basis for deciding whether they are a good person or a person of value. Replies usually involve the idea of being a giving and often loving person. Interesting, the apparent antithetical concept of never doing anything harmful, will often be proclaimed. At this point, many people might announce they now realize that, ultimately, trust (if it involves a sense of goodness or value in oneself) can only be bestowed on oneself, by oneself. Because the sense of value is a universal preoccupation, I promptly put forth the proposition *All Human Beings Are of Value.*

If one conditionally accepts this proposition, one must accept that there is something intrinsic in *the nature of humanness* that is of value. *If all human beings are of value, the essence of the state of humanness must have value.* We are now confronted with a question which usually brings a hushed silence: *What is the essence of humanness?*

One of the most crucial factors in a clear understanding of what constitutes the concept of essence is the dimension of time. The essence of a thing, by definition, must always be present during the life of the object. That means it is there from the first instant until the last instant of its existence.

Another crucial factor in the concept of essence is the dimension of permanence or sameness. Whatever the essence of a thing, it remains throughout the life of the thing to be exactly the same and cannot change for any period or moment of time.

Returning now to the statement that the essence of humanness has value, we can restate this as Whatever it is that makes each of us have value, it is there from the first instant of our life until our demise, and that the determining factor never changes at any time during our life.

We are now faced with the task of how we go about searching for this "elan vital," or essence of humanness.

Let us reduce this to the most basic elements. As a general principle, we can usually find an object in its simplest or least complicated state, if we very carefully examine it at its point of origin or at its very first moment of existence.

What is it that is most elemental, crucial, and universal within every newborn infant from its first moment of life? The essence present in each new being at that earliest moment is need. It may take some time and further clarification for the utmost significance of this discovery to be fully appreciated. What I suggest with this observation is that our civilization has essentially been going 180 degrees in the wrong direction for more than 2,000 years.

Modern Western culture has been attempting to determine the value of individuals, groups, societies, and entire civilizations by its accomplishments or performances. A tragic irony may now present itself upon close examination. Have you never questioned why all the societies or civilizations that we study, revere or esteem most, such as the Greek, Roman, or Egyptian societies all destroyed themselves? In these examples, clearly, accomplishment is not ultimately a true measure of natural success or endurance. Therefore, I propose the following.

The value of a human life is based on the needs of that human and has nothing to do with performance. Again, the essence of humanness (the basis of its value) cannot change for even one instant *from the very first moment of life until the final moment of life.* The essence is need, and need alone throughout life remains the principle that determines the value of humanness.

Let's return to the example of the woman who felt the lack of, and therefore the need for, trust. If we accept the fundamental essence of humanness as need, we may now more clearly understand how she alone can bestow the feeling of trust of her own value or goodness on herself. In the end, she can only arrive at this feeling of self-value through her own experience of feeling fulfillment of her needs. Trust, therefore, arises out of her feeling that she can and will sufficiently fulfill her human needs. She can now be at peace as she seeks to fulfill her needs, aware that her needs are the living basis of her value. In Chapter Six, we will examine the effects of this example on her jealous husband. Once more, let me state emphatically that human value has nothing to do with performance. Need is the determining factor.

Dr. Jerome Schulte

Human needs
are experienced
through our
feelings.

Chapter 2
On Human Need

Synopsis:

Following Chapter One's postulate that need is the essence and the determinant of the value of humanness, an exploration is necessary of the essence of need. An introduction into the concept of contradiction and Hegel's statement "Something has vital force only when it contains contradiction" is an important foundation to understand need.

We use the dimensions again of permanence or sameness and timelessness, but now with their contradictions of difference and the moment. We postulate the essence of all human need is contained in and experienced through our feelings.

As a result of inherent difficulties studying feelings, the author provides the concept of "The 5 Arenas of Feelings," a set of five feelings and their contradictions, as a method of studying needs on an individual basis.

If at first you experience a sense of relief and peace when arriving at the concept of need as the essence of Humanness, shortly afterwards you may feel the ominous shadow of a larger dilemma. Once we begin to explore the realm of essence as it applies to human beings, one very quickly senses a peculiar never-ending feeling. Yes, it feels as one could go on and on forever. Perhaps we *do*. On the *possibility* we do, I find another question arising out of what seems the apparent final answer.

Just as there is always that sense of unrevealed substance when one tries to know the intimate nature of a person or thing, you may now realize there were aspects of the opening chapter in the Essence of Humanness that were simplistic. Those who are greatly concerned with the issue of abortion and the question of when human life begins and when it has a soul or has value most assuredly would have been on the alert. You must read this entire work to have your answer.

If we are to go on with our search for an understanding of ourselves, we must now modify the realm of our investigation, This in itself brings up an interesting and, I think, very vital question. If we propose to study the essence of human need, are we figuratively getting closer to the core of everything (or *anything,* whichever term suits you) or are we getting more distant from the core? Restating my earlier statement in the form of a question: Are we really expanding or narrowing the realm of our investigation?

If you drop a pebble into water, watch the ever-expanding concentric circles, and try intimately to know the nature of the occurrence, do you work back to the initial circle and the pebble or do you concentrate on the radiating circles outward? I believe the answer is that naturally one does both, individually and simultaneously. It is exactly the same with humanness!

I think we are now ready to approach the question of what is the essence of human need. Keep in mind the substantive portion of this work is a study of essential human needs from an evolutionary, developmental, life cycle framework. I am therefore defining certain limitations but I feel the need to establish a philosophical and theoretically sound framework to build upon.

What is the essence of human need?

It is crucial that we first approach the question of methodology. The following quotation from Hegel has profoundly influenced this work. "Something has vital force only when it contains contradiction." The basic methodology in this work is the study of the process of the forces of contradiction.

In the first chapter I introduced the concept of time or timelessness and the concept of permanence or sameness. I now would like to enlarge both of those concepts and include their immediate contradictions. The contradiction of <u>sameness</u> is <u>difference</u>. The contradiction of <u>timelessness</u> is the <u>moment.</u> Our experience with human need tells us that the essence or sameness of need is always present or timeless. However, the immediate quality or character of the need may and will be different from moment to moment. To know the complete essence of a thing we are forced to study the contradictions contained within the <u>essence of all things</u>. Ultimately that includes studying what we do not need.

Next I would like to introduce the concept I discovered to be most vital to appreciate a work of art. One must approach a work very closely until one feels the vitality in it. One must also then stand back from it to feel what is and what is not in perspective to the world. In a sense, the work is a part of and at the same moment not a part of what is outside it. I trust you now have a feeling for the concept of closeness versus distance.

Another important concept in the above example is somewhat more subtle. The artist and his work of art are at times almost indistinguishably one and the same and yet they are separate. The most beautiful example: an expectant mother and her child are, at the moment of conception, one and the same in unity and yet already they are separate. Couples, deeply in love, at the moment of mutual simultaneous orgasm may feel united in every way and yet they are separate. Amazingly, the concept of separateness versus unity is now a part of you and yet it has an identity separate from you.

Finally, I humbly need to apprise you of the final important concept required in our work. No matter how you and I may feel we now know something, do we really? Stated more simply: "At the moment we finally feel we know, deep inside the truth emerges that we do not fully know." This the concept of knowing versus not knowing.

As we approach the study of human need we will use these five balances or scales or sets of contradictions to weigh, to measure, to get to a beginning of knowledge.

Before moving on I would like to give you a few practical tools that may help us to get at "the stuff" we want to study. These are practical little approaches I have developed after 41 years of much interaction with my patients. They are steps I go through to get my patients ready to experience their humanness.

First: Intellectual insight, in and of itself, isn't worth a damn.
            It doesn't change anything.

Second: When you run out of things to do, think, or talk about.
            Something meaningful is more likely to happen.

Third: First you feel and then you'll know.
            Feeling is the essence of human need. Feeling, as I use the word semantically is a dynamic process that exists:
            in the moment and through eternity.
            that is always present as a feeling, but may have distinctly different qualities any moment.
            which requires closeness for a full, unique appreciation, but also requires distance to put
            into a perspective with the rest of life.
            which we will feel at moments is literally a part of us and we a part of it—only to find we and it are and need to be separate in the next moment.
            which we, at moments, will know and understand its presence, and yet never fully know because of our unconscious.

The five arenas of this dynamic process will be in motion simultaneously for every need, because "process is content."

Five Arenas of Feeling

Moment	versus	Duration
Difference	versus	Sameness
Closeness	versus	Distance
Unity	versus	Separateness
Knowing	versus	Not Knowing

An everyday example of the 5 arenas of feelings in coming to an understanding of the need for nourishment as experienced through the feeling of hunger.

As a student in class at 11 a.m., you suddenly experience a "moment" of a feeling of hunger, which may first be experienced as a pang of discomfort in your stomach. Stay in touch with that experience over the next hour before you will be free to go to the cafeteria. Thus we will study the experience of hunger over the "duration" of that hour. You may use these same processes during the next several occasions that this need for nourishment arises to study whether the "first moment" presents with a "sameness" or "difference." The next three times you experience hunger, observe if its first moment is felt in the same manner or in a different manner.

What is the nature of the occasion when there is a "sameness" in presentation and, by the same token, what is the nature of the occasion when there is a "difference" in the presentation of that feeling of hunger?

Now it is noon and you approach the cafeteria line. You can see and smell the food, yet there is usually a glass barrier or some form of "distance" between you and the food. Study your experience of hunger from this perspective. Now you are seated, ready to take in the visual and olfactory components of the food from the position of "closeness."

Next you place the food in your mouth and on your tongue initiating the taste buds and mastication process. However, there is still a physical state of "separateness" of the food from your full being at the initiation of this process. Nevertheless, soon the food or nourishment begins to become one in "unity" with you.

How often have you then experienced that you "knew" this was the form of nourishment you needed and that the hunger feeling had been quantitatively and qualitatively fulfilled? But wait, and how often and after consuming a meal then experienced the feeling of still being hungry? You are now aware of the concept of "not knowing" something you had previously believed you knew.

I encourage you to keep a diary for a week of your experiences with this most basic repetitive human need. You may be amazed at how much deeper an understanding you will have of one aspect of your basic personality.

Dr. Jerome Schulte

Ninety-nine percent of the
people spend ninety-nine
percent of their life's
energy running away
from themselves
and their feelings.

Chapter 3
On Feeling

Synopsis:

If the essence of humanness is need and the driving force in need is feelings, one can postulate the driving force behind all human feelings is the need for growth.

Therefore, the core of humanness is the need to grow through feelings. Its contradiction is the process of dying. The role of culture regarding societal growth and change will also be explored.

If you have felt that I have taken you "around the barnyard" in the first two chapters, this next segment will most certainly tax your patience. We will attempt to finally get to the essence of feeling. Prepare for some difficult work ahead!

Life frequently involves us in events seemingly determined by the phenomena of chance or fate. While studying for one of many board examinations, I happened to review the mortality statistics for the United States. Some very obvious, "known-to-all" simple statistics and "facts" initiated a series of reverberations in my mind. This was akin to the never-ending concentric circles created by a pebble dropped in a pool of water. I was struck by the fact that the average life in this country is 75-80 years. We have documented evidence—dramatically portrayed by studies done in Russia—that the human body, with the aid of modern medical knowledge and technology, can certainly sustain a life at least twice that duration.

Carefully studying the causes of death from a psychological viewpoint, it became apparent that the majority of deaths are a direct result from psychological afflictions (which also include physical deaths that modern medicine recognizes as being initiated by psychological conflicts) or maladies of the "spirit." To be specific, the majority of people die premature deaths that are the result of unresolved psychological conflicts. In fact, we ultimately destroy ourselves!

If we very seriously consider this to be a fact, a very uncomfortable feeling must begin to boil inside of you as it did in me. What is the crux of this and what are the means to avert this universal tragedy that has been in existence throughout the history of civilization?

Allow me to again confront you with a simple tragedy with which every physician is ultimately confronted. If and when we (or another patient) die, a physician will sign a death certificate which briefly lists the cause(s) of our demise. For the majority of us it will either state that our death was: suicide by some method of our individual choice; homicide, the murderer and his victim; accidental death; that our death was caused by some physical illness, whose name will average nine syllables phonetically; that is essentially self-induced. (Intellectual insight in and of itself, isn't worth a damn. It doesn't change anything.) **Indeed, we actually kill ourselves!** Only the reluctance of my medical colleagues to consider psychological causation in cancer, viral diseases, multiple sclerosis, etc., makes me use the word *majority,* rather than nearly *universal* when speaking of how many of us kill ourselves.

I said the majority of people die premature deaths as the result of unresolved psychological conflicts. What do you imagine would occur if those psychological conflicts were resolved? Is it possible that we might not die prematurely, that instead we might go on living, and that as a result of conflicts being resolved we might be able to move on in an **expanded** way?

Let us return to the central theme of our work. If the essence of

humanness is **need** and the driving force in need are **feelings,** how can we integrate our new awareness of the forces promoting life versus death? If we hold that the essence of **need** in human life is **feeling,** then unresolved conflicts would appear to hinge on our relative lack of attainment of *specific* feelings. This at first may be a difficult concept to grasp for those unfamiliar with the medical diseases from which most of us supposedly die. For the clinically unfamiliar, one of the first "facts" a medical student learns is 3 out of 4 who enter a medical office has a problem that is essentially in their heads. No honest; experienced physician will deny this odd truth.

Simply put, if we fail to succeed to attain important feelings, our being can only respond to that lack or deprivation through some contradictory destructive feeling which ultimately leads to one of two conclusions. First, to an act of suicide (directly or indirectly) by arranging our own accident or homicide; second, turning the contradictory destructive feeling into our physical body thereby developing a physical affliction which eventually leads to our premature death.

Return now again to the question of what would occur if our needs were positively resolved or fulfilled through some important feeling. Is it conceivable that we could actually transition to lives of greater duration in a more expanded, more qualitative manner?

I now propose the essence of feeling is "Growth." The contradiction to Growth, which I have attempted to describe in stark cold terms, is Death! (We can only begin to fully know the nature of a thing by studying its contradiction.) I am saying that the core of humanness is the need to grow through feelings. The impact of this impressed upon each of us is if at any point we fail to grow in terms of feelings or experience, the result is we begin to die.

Only if we promote our human essence or value through fulfillment of our needs of progressive attainment of essential feelings can we continue to grow. Ultimately, a successful strategy that can be implemented by society will result in an expanded, longer-lived, healthier, and more productive world society.

This process of the development of feelings proceeds in a positive growth manner or in a destructive manner at each and every step. You will discover a certain predictability to the form and method of suicide (including the type of medical illness we choose to inflict on ourselves). Each person chooses whether she or he chooses to abandon human growth.

There is an even deeper mystery that involves the process that something must be dying while something is simultaneously growing. Dying can be a positive process if it is not premature and if it is intimately tied to a growth process. Our safety zone must continually die, because risk is an *essential* attribute of growth.

In Plato's *New Republic,* which became the prototype for Christian (especially the Roman Catholic) churches and essentially dominated the course of Western civilization for nearly 2,000 years, that the ultimate need in humanness (the feeling of ever-continuing growth) was overlooked. Plato's Utopia was essentially a static system destined for failure. The Church, ultimately a group of human beings, seems to be gaining awareness of its humanness of late, and seems at times to be desperately scrambling to regain a stable foundation.

It has often been noted that culture is the most difficult aspect to change in human beings. Barriers to change are built into cultural traits and patterns over time. A major component of nearly all cultural patterns is religious beliefs. They are inculcated with mandates that exceed human capability and are often the most resistant aspect of culture to allow change. Most wars have emerged, in part, over a conflict in cultural religious beliefs or, at minimum, those beliefs have been used to support the validity of wars.

Currently we see how Islamic radicals have taken advantage of democratic freedoms in Europe and the USA to insinuate themselves into a country. Then they resort to terrorism to acquire power with an ultimate plan to bring the country under Muslim control. One wonders if resolutions to the Jewish-Arab conflict and Muslim-Christian conflict will ever be found.

Societies need change. An example worthy of study is the change in American culture during the era of Justice Sandra Day O'Connor's tenure on the Supreme Court, which has traditionally been expected to set precedents on newly arising conflicts that could be evaluated on their merits of long-standing traditions and culture. Justice O'Connor has, in effect, memorialized the concept of "the current weight of public opinion" in many of her decisions that have been the swing votes of many 5-4 decisions. For example, Roe vs. Wade interpretations regard preserving "freedom of choice" and perhaps most dramatically in the issue of "the death penalty for the mentally retarded" on which she observed a change in "the current weight of public opinion" within the brief span of 5 years. She was clearly an advocate for the need and ability of society to change. From a strict constructionist viewpoint, she was an anathema leaving many to feel the power of the traditional courts was taken away, and every decision of state and federal appellate courts had to go back to the Supreme Court to be decided.

Growth for individual human beings is an ongoing struggle, even more for a society, ever more for our world society. One of the most vital accomplishments in this direction occurred after WWII as a result of the Nuremberg War Crimes Trials with the adoption of the Universal Declaration of Human Rights[2] in 1948 by the United Nations. They are moral rights of the highest order, grounded in the equal moral dignity of each person. Human rights are a special class of rights held by a person simply by virtue of being human. Although these rights are implemented slowly worldwide because of multicultural standards in countries throughout the world, the new universal code has been established. International law is clearly gaining importance as evidenced by the US Supreme Court in its 2005 decision[11] abolishing the death penalty for minors, citing the international legal community pressure as an overriding influence.

The flowcharts on the following pages capture the essence of humanness via the pattern of human emotional growth.

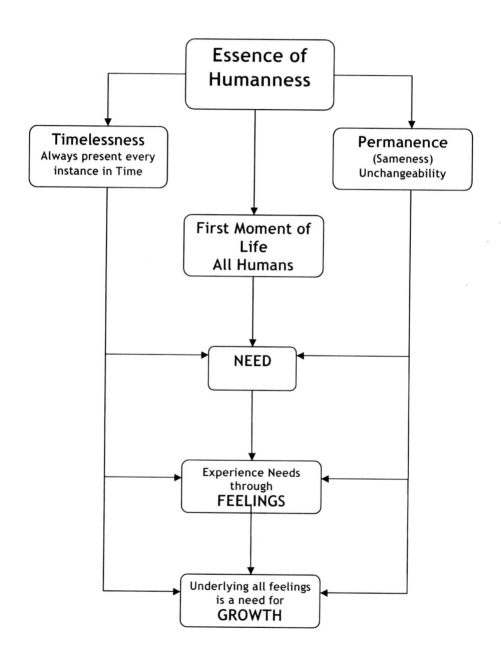

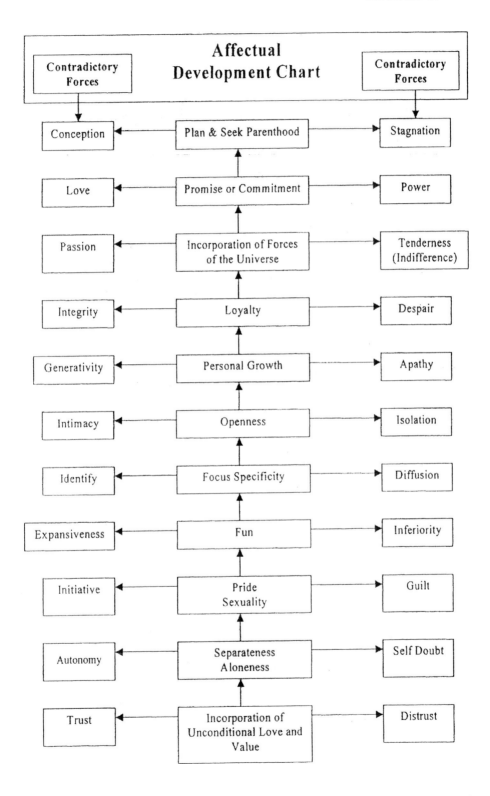

There is nothing
that can exist in life
with vital force that
does not contain
contradiction.

It is a measure of
that force that the
contradiction can be
grasped and
endured.

Hegel

Chapter 4
Trust Versus Distrust

Synopsis:

The critical needs of the first year of life are explored from an Eriksonian evolutionary developmental perspective: "There is nothing that can exist in life with vital force that does not contain contradiction. It is a measure of that force that the contradiction can be grasped and endured."

The first essential need is a feeling of value that must be experienced, just because one exists. This need cannot be earned. This feeling of value is an outcome of unconditional love for which I have coined the phrase "the magical elixir of life." Furthermore, the successful experience of unconditional love is dependent on it being experienced through human touch. Trust of the feeling of unconditional love provides necessary vital energy. Because no parent is perfect, there is a natural phenomenon of the child struggling with the contradictory feelings of distrust. One of my principles states that in each and every need in life there must be a "sufficient satisfactory fulfillment of the need" for the child to move to the next growth step.

The process of incorporation is described with its contradiction at the time of the 8-month separation anxiety syndrome.

✳

There are many published scales of human development. I have always found Eric Erickson's scale based on feelings to be most useful.

Recalling the example of the married woman who felt the need for trust and my closing statement in the first chapter. She could only come to a feeling of value of herself through the feeling of trust that her human needs can and will be sufficiently fulfilled. We are now faced with the task of learning how one can achieve this feeling of trust.

I believe the world has been quite widely exposed by now to Dr. LeBoyer's method of childbirth which, hopefully, will become one of the most powerful and influential forces in changing human life. However, it is always amazing, and often sad, to see how much time truly powerful developments require for acceptance. Dr. LeBoyer's method certainly has the potential to enhance the relative degree of trust in human beings. The impact of that could be astounding for our civilization and the emerging world culture. The importance of Dr. LeBoyer's method of childbirth essentially is that it enhances the feelings of safety and security for the child as he or she enters the world as contrasted to a feeling of danger that heretofore we were most all greeted with at our time of entry.

The first eight months of life are very critical for human development. We are quite totally dependent on others to fulfill our needs for security, nourishment, warmth, caring, affection, and love. Furthermore, there is nothing we can do of consequence to fulfill our needs other than attempt to make our needs known. Indeed, we may cry, which may bring a response of caring and understanding or, too often, a response of irritation and other negative feelings.

For our needs to be successfully fulfilled in those first months requires the love of someone for us simply because we exist and who believes we are of value simply because we exist. Eric Fromm's term of unconditional love for the feeling that most often exists between mother and child is perfectly descriptive.

This feeling of unconditional love is the sine qua non for the development of basic trust. Let us consider the feeling of unconditional love on the framework of the five analytical balances.

The moment at which this is at its highest peak could well be with the infant on its mother's breast fulfilled and about to drift off to sleep. At that moment, there might well be a feeling of unity in the first months of life, to be gradually replaced by a feeling of closeness in later months on such an occasion. The feeling of knowing unconditional love would be present at that moment. Each time the child nurses, there would be some feeling of *sameness* of unconditional love as well as some feelings of *difference*, depending on the mother's mood at different occasions. The child would also begin to experience the contradictory separateness at moments when the nursing process might be unfortunately interrupted. Spinoza once said, "Nothing can be understood in isolation." I would like to add, "No feeling can be completely known without some experience of it in isolation and sharing."

An infant at the mother's breast, taking in her milk, and accompanied by the feeling of unconditional love is the "magical elixir" of life. It is truly magical because once incorporated into the infant, it can be used repeatedly in life and yet one can never use up a single drop. It is literally there for life to be used continually, but never consumed or destroyed. Yes, it may be hidden by other feelings, but always remains and accounts for many of the survivors in infancy who otherwise would have expired or experienced tragedy.

As the number of moments the child experiences mother's unconditional love mounts, the more the feeling moves from a position of being momentary to having duration. Its feeling of unity with mother will be quite pronounced for the first six to eight months of life in breast feeding or cuddling and bundling. When the child goes through the process of separation at eight months, it will frequently want to return to the security of mother's arms to comfortably deal with the contradictory experiences of Unity vs. Separateness.

The game of peek-a-boo is effective during separation anxiety. It allows the infant to practice again and again the experience of separateness for brief periods of time, yet be able to re-experience unity with his/her parent or love object.

Another excellent activity to introduce to a child at this age are picture puzzles that stimulate the drive to achieve or restore a feeling of completeness or unity in the face of incompleteness or separation. Repetition will consolidate and enhance many emerging intellectual functions.

At this time, although it certainly happens earlier in life, the child will begin to know the feeling of closeness and its contradictory feeling of distance. We often laugh and talk about how the child first separates itself by a room, then the backyard, and then the neighborhood. Perhaps you are beginning to appreciate the subtlety of how we begin to experience life and how, through the process of contradictory feelings, the infant begins to gain a sense of itself.

Gradually the child realizes that it is the one who is feeling the presence of contradiction in its existence and that it endures it, survives it, and gains strength within, through the realization that it has endured the contradiction.

To quote Hegel: "There is nothing that can exist in life that has vital force that does not contain contradiction. It is a measure of that force that the contradiction can be grasped and endured."

By now you must also be beginning to realize how the child's experience of life multiplies at an enormous rate, considering how each feeling experience of life ultimately is played out through the five contradictory sets of balances.

Remember, no human being is perfect. It is unrealistic for us to expect that any mother can perfectly, at all times, provide unconditional love. Just as a work of art has its imperfections and gains value because of it, so is it potentially true with humanness.

Again we realize the depth of Hegel's insight that it is the contradictions that are the source of our vitality. The contradiction of trust is distrust. When the child's feeling of unconditional love evaporates during times of nonfulfillment or frustration of its early needs, the feeling of anger or rage arises. Anger is the second most powerful feeling that a human being can experience. The ability to express anger is of the utmost importance in the development of a balanced, healthy personality.

If the infant's anger is not taken in and responded to adequately, extremely powerful destructive forces are set in motion. An infant who is allowed to scream for hours and left in isolation will slowly begin to block out of its awareness the need for love, nurture, and comfort through the use of suppression, initially, and then by overt denial of its feelings of need.

The needs remain within and, therefore, so does the rage which is suppressed and denied, For some infants, the denial used is so profound that the ultimate result may often be crib death; for others, it sets in motion any one, or a combination of very destructive psychological or physiological mechanisms.

The needs remain. A child may find itself swinging back and forth between these contradictory feelings of trust and distrust. Hopefully the scales will lean to the side of trust that its needs will be sufficiently fulfilled. With the feeling of trust a child may find value as a human being.

As you may recall, there is a predictability to the method of suicide one chooses, if one fails to evolve through the growth process. If the scales should lean in the direction of distrust rather than trust, certain possibilities begin to arise. These possibilities become more clearly definable as the result of each step in the growth process begins to manifest in the child's development.

As a general statement, the body responds in a general total body manner in the beginning and becomes more specialized in its responses as development proceeds. The mouth, skin, eyes, lungs, stomach, hands, the generalized nervous system, and endocrine system are the areas most specifically involved in the fulfillment of needs in the first year of life. These are the areas that can become the focus for physical illness through the mediation of the autonomic nervous system.

Obesity and other oral fixations such as smoking and even some cases of alcoholism have their origins in the first year of life and are physiological expressions of rage. I believe many dermatological conditions, various forms of asthma, multiple sclerosis, and other generalized neurological conditions also originate in the first year, or the ground work is set for their later development, if growth is not sufficiently successful. I firmly believe countless forms of cancer are merely evidence of and elaborations of severe degrees of unattainment of fulfillment of need for specific feelings.

Also, as a consequence of distrust gaining the upper hand over trust, a basis is established for the most damaging psychoses, major personality disorders, and antisocial or psychopathic conditions. The natural history of all these afflictions includes and concludes with premature death, often for one or more people.

In these conditions we can also see the insidious onset of a number of very powerful processes that, if left unchecked, hold potential for great destructiveness. Consider briefly the possibility of the mother (or person assuming the mothering role) in a personal state of psychosis, antisocial personality, or severe regression through depression. The mother may be driven to form an attachment to the child to gain a feeling of aliveness through the child. A form of parasitism may in this way develop between the mother and child. Each literally feels the need for the other for its own survival. This process can be any relative degree from vicariously drawing pleasure from the child by the mother to parasitism of the child by the mother to a beginning symbiotic parasitism of mother and child.

Very bluntly, if there is an absence or deficiency of unconditional love one receives in the first year of life, it will have a lasting effect until steps are taken to fulfill the need. The relative deficiency will impede successful completion of each succeeding steps of evolutionary growth.

Accordingly, we are faced with the continued cycle of insufficient growth, generation after generation, unless something or someone dramatically alters this pattern.

Consider the magnitude of the impact on all successive stages of human growth, if a solid feeling of unconditional love is established in the first year of life. The trust that one is of value and will always be of value, no matter what occurs in life, gives an unshakable foundation on which to build. How can one be certain that it is unconditional love and not some form of deception that, in truth, has hidden attached conditions?

An important developmental process worth highlighting at this stage of development is childcare. Babysitters become a vital element at this stage. Inherently, parents need separate time together to refuel their relationship. This separate time provides an excellent opportunity for a child to experience separation for a longer period and foster enhancement of trust with new individuals. In addition, having a new arena to strengthen his/her skills, the child will deal with the contradiction of trust versus distrust. A careful selection of these new individuals cannot be overemphasized. Grandparents, loving individuals, can fulfill an important role at this point. Symbolism also provides a measure of security through these periods of separateness and aloneness. "The security blanket" or stuffed animal can be a helpful tool, if used positively.

Working mothers in today's society who are parent and necessary wage-earner have additional challenges in this area. Certainly, childcare availability at the worksite needs to be strongly promoted. Studies need to be conducted that support the concept of reduced health care costs as an incentive for employers to provide this service.

Newborns are essentially 100% feeling. They learn to separate truth from deception and are never really deceived for very long. Consider, for example, the respected professional held in esteem by his community, but held in disdain by his children. What is it they know that busy adults seem to gloss over? Gradually you will come to appreciate my one basic tenet, "First you feel, then you know." The supply of people in the world able to provide unconditional love is limited, so refer to Chapter 12 for a more comprehensive understanding of this important arena.

On Developing Trust Through Unconditional Love

Unconditional love is the feeling that one has worth simply because one exists. It does not have to be earned; **it cannot be earned**. There is only one medium through which a feeling of unquestionable worth, just by virtue of existence, can be obtained. That medium is the sense of touch. If one is very perceptive, as a child is, then there is one sense that does not lie and which one can trust over all other senses: the sense of touch.

Not only am I speaking of direct tactile human touch to another human, but I am also speaking of what is colloquially termed "picking up all the vibrations of one's immediate environment." If we enlarged this concept to the ultimate, one can almost include picking up the vibrations of the universe as experienced by the acutely psychotic individual. I will never forget one young schizophrenic teenager, who during a therapy session which was suddenly interrupted by the shattering noise and vibrations of an air hammer at work several blocks away, exclaimed, "stop hammering on me." What you see by this example is the shattering effect total openness to the universe can have on a human being who does not have a solidly established sense of its own being and conviction of self-worth.

Specifically, the human act necessary to establish sufficient unconditional love is the act of being held by another human being. There is no substitute. Furthermore, the feeling that one's existence has worth must be a part of that act of being held.

This was demonstrated in early studies conducted by Rene Spitz[15] from the University of Colorado, who was puzzled by an usually high death rate in infants placed at birth in orphanages. His studies found that the significant factor was a deficient amount of being held and experiencing human touch with the necessary accompanying unconditional love.

One needs to consider the criteria that determine the difference or uniqueness in human beings, namely, the quantity and quality of each individual's needs. Some day an enterprising study will be conducted, and science may study the differing qualities and quantities of the need for human touch in individual infants. Ultimately the tracking of where it is experienced with unconditional love would be worthy of a Nobel Prize. For those finding themselves deficient in the feeling of unconditional love, there is no turning away from the need to secure a **sufficient** amount of being held by someone capable of bestowing a feeling that human life is of worth by virtue of its presence.

I must make it clear that being held, by itself alone, will not cure severe mental illness, personality disorders or neuroses. It *will* cure a deficiency of unconditional love and therefore a sense of trust that one's needs in life can be met. No disorder, that involves a lack of feeling of unconditional love and trust of one's worth, can be cured without the person *first* experiencing sufficient amounts of holding and being held.

There is a logical order in human growth, and a sufficient fulfillment of the specific need must be accomplished in each step before there will be a true resolution of that step. There can be a degree of work accomplished in many areas while awaiting the completion of the work at the specific step at issue, but there can be no true resolution of any new step until all of the preceding steps have been resolved in their natural sequence.

Once there has been sufficient holding, it becomes possible that an individual can reinforce the feeling of unconditional love just by the presence of the giving, holding person. As the experience of unconditional love grows, there is an increasing distance over which this feeling can be perceived. As we go through life, it is inevitable we will encounter many kinds of conflict and stress, at which time it may be necessary to replenish our reservoir of unconditional love. I have in fact become convinced that as we attempt each new progressive step of growth we must, to some relative degree, fuel ourselves by retouching and reworking all of the previous steps of growth. We need to be aware that the sense of touch can also be utilized by the mother or the child to set up a parasitic attachment.

The sense of touch can, therefore, basically out of early deprivation, become a powerful manipulative tool to control one's environment. Touch, through its use, or through denial or rejection of its use, is the most powerful, yet least understood, of all our senses.

Autonomy

The ability to be alone and,
when necessary, to stand
self-sufficiently.

Chapter 5
Autonomy versus Self-Doubt

Synopsis:

I have formulated an inherent truth of one's existence proclaiming life is a singular journey. As unconditional love is the requisite for the development I define worth or value, aloneness is essential for the development of autonomy. I define autonomy as the "ability to stand alone, self-sufficiently in the world when necessary."

The contradictory force to autonomy is self-doubt. It can become quite destructive, if based on a lack of sufficient sense of trust of one's value will be met by others.

The negativism of the 18-month to 3-year-old child is illustrative of an infant's desire for an initial sense of autonomy.

In summary: Through unconditional love and trust one is able to achieve a feeling of worth or value. Autonomy experienced through aloneness establishes a feeling of self-worth

*

As we consider the next natural and essential step of human growth, it is important that you have an appreciation of the cumulative effect each step has upon the subsequent step. The relative degree to which we successfully fulfill the crucial need of each step and come to a resolution of the contradictions inherent in the specific feeling is reflected in the measure of vitality or vital force we have available in each succeeding step.

Assume the child has been sufficiently successful attaining

unconditional love, it has a trust of its own value, and its needs can be fulfilled in life. As already described, the point arrives when the feeling of unity with mother begins to be dissolved, a sense of separateness begins to occur, and the child is able to move into new horizons, through its own locomotion.

A prominent growth spurt of the prefrontal brain lobes takes place toward the end of the first year of life, at the beginning of the toddler stage. The outcome of this neural growth depends on the nature and amount of nurturing from the child's primary caregiver. Rich neural connections are established between the forward-most section of the prefrontal lobes developed during the first year of life and the highest region of the emotional (old mammalian) brain established in utero.

This connection, called the orbital-frontal loop centered behind the orbit of the eye, is responsible for influencing a person's relationships and mental capacities in life. And further, the "affective tone" or emotional state experienced by the toddler during the exploratory period after age one determines the nature of the orbital-frontal loop and its ability to function.

Allan Stone in "Affect Regulation and the Origin of the Self: The Neurobiology of Emotional Development," explains a toddler's emotional state during this time of world exploration determines whether or not the orbital-frontal connection is established and used or largely lost. He describes how the orbital-frontal linkage is entwined with the care a toddler receives and how this, in turn, determines the lifelong shape and character of that child's world view, mind set, sense of self, impulse control, and ability to relate to others. It is impossible to overestimate the importance of the orbital-frontal function.

Neural brain spurts occur in other parts of our brain at age four and age seven, with additional shifts in brain function at ages nine and eleven leading to windows of opportunity for intelligences and abilities to unfold relative to the neural modules of the brain ready for development.

Integral to the actor idea of the child moving about by its own locomotion is the feeling of *aloneness* it gradually becomes aware of in so doing. As unconditional love was requisite for the development of basic trust, so is aloneness essential for the development of autonomy. We spend much of our lives involved with people in countless forms of activity. I find that people often lose sight of a crucial fact: Life is inherently a singular journey.

Imagine yourself as the young child toddling around the yard and finding yourself behind a bush that obscures a view of the house. Suddenly, you sense the feeling of aloneness. Depending on the degree of previously established trust that you had experienced, you might yet feel a sense of being safe and whole as opposed to feeling unsafe and even on the verge of shattering emotionally. The contradictions of this phase of development, therefore, are between a secure feeling of being able to stand alone as a singular person in the world (which is Autonomy) and its opposite feeling, self-doubt.

Again, let us consider the crucial feeling of aloneness on the analytical balances. The child, standing behind the bush, may be experiencing its first moment of aloneness. Indeed, it will likely choose only to experience it for that brief moment, initially. As the number of these moments or encounters with this experience increases, it becomes aware of the tendency for that feeling to reoccur, or the development of a permanence of that feeling within.

The child will also, as experience with it increases, realize a certain sameness always present in the experience of aloneness. And yet, the experience of self always has a difference because of the process of growth or lack of growth or regression that has occurred.

Each experience of the feeling of aloneness is felt with intensity of some magnitude, which is related to how close we allow ourselves to come to a full unobstructed experience of it as opposed to what distance we attempt to interpose between it and ourselves. In the experience of aloneness, we most powerfully feel the contradiction between a sense of unity and separateness with a specific feeling.

Here, I would like to shift to the most powerful experience of the contradiction to autonomy, which is self-doubt. The child who has reached this point in life, with a grossly insufficient amount of unconditional love and a rather marked feeling of distrust of its value, will experience the feeling of aloneness in a most overwhelming manner. If this child becomes one in unity with its feeling of aloneness, the descriptive phrase for this horrendous experience is called "the terror of the soul." To experience the feeling of total aloneness on a background that involves a feeling of nearly total worthlessness, or absence of value, at night in blackness, lays bare even the existence of one's identity (self) or soul to doubt. Because the feeling of creation in some form is always present in such instances, can the survival feeling of separateness, of such aloneness, have a redeeming value.

On the side of autonomy, can you imagine the power in a constructive direction, if the feeling of unity with one's aloneness can be experienced in peace on a foundation of bountiful trust in one's value? To be one with oneself in aloneness, is to know oneself. Yet, there is always a condition of not knowing, which will be dealt with in the last two chapters of the book.

Now we address the forms of suicide that might manifest, if the feeling of autonomy is not attained. Most completed direct suicides or indirect suicides (by arranging one's own homicide) have their origins dynamically at this crucial point in life. Because the intensity of the feeling of self in aloneness is so great, we can also expect things such as essential hypertension, hyperthyroidism, arrhythmias, migraine headaches, insomnia, and their contradictions, such as hypotension, hypothyroidism, somnolence, somnambulism, diabetes, and other endocrine dysfunctions to develop as life goes on.

Two of the most common, sometimes daily uncomfortable feelings of life, have their origins linked to the struggle between autonomy and self-doubt. Specifically, I am referring to worry and fear. Worry is a feeling that expresses an awareness of one being relatively unsure of one's sense of self-sufficiency to deal comfortably with an event. Fear is a feeling that harm, destruction, or some sense of loss might come to our person or to what is perceived as a fragile feeling of autonomy or self-sufficiency. Fear in an exaggerated state is often described as "feeling as if one might totally shatter."

What a joy it is to see a child who can be happy, playing alone, and being able to enjoying its play with others. Human are powerful contradictions. They are, by nature being gregarious and yet singular beings. A child who has unsuccessfully attained autonomy through aloneness, will begin to show significant signs of withdrawal. It is vital that the understanding mother, realizing the importance of the experience of aloneness, will allow room and time for these experiences, yet be available to reaffirm that there can always be someone available in life to nurture as it is needed.

Perhaps the most easily recognized evidence of the child insisting on a sense of autonomy in its thoughts, feelings, and actions is the well known negativism of the 18-month to 3-year-old. The child must be in opposition to everything, in conflict with everyone at times, to insist on a chance to be autonomous.

On Developing Autonomy

I find in our present day American society that autonomy is one of the most difficult traits to develop. How difficult it seems to be to achieve solitude in aloneness! Even for the individual ready to take on the task of autonomy, it is hard, at first, to achieve a true state of aloneness. Imagine a day by yourself, away from all other people: no TV, radio, food, drink, books, magazines, pets, traffic, noise. In his marvelous book, *Centennial*, James Michener describes how throughout the history of the developing West, man often found it necessary to go off alone by himself. Michener seemed a bit perplexed about this. I find it very natural because only in that way can a person experience his/her own inner self. The direction one must take if one wishes to work on developing the trait of autonomy is therefore simple. You must begin to spend time with yourself in aloneness—total aloneness.

The direction is simple. The accomplishment of it is extremely difficult and can be painful. Many people find it helpful to get away for a weekend—alone—to a favorite location or hideaway. As one's comfortableness increases over time, one can be alone with oneself in solitude almost anywhere. I have found it helpful for many people, when they begin to develop this trait, to lie down with their eyes closed and visualize their minds as a blank movie screen. It is not easy at first to totally empty your mind and hold it there in a blank state keeping out all the background noise, the "garbage" of everyday life. We are, of course, borrowing from the natural state that occurs during sleep and dreams. The object is to recapture that state and yet be awake.

You can begin now to realize how a solid sense of feeling of worth and trust that one's needs in life can be met is a prerequisite for this approach to produce meaningful results. A therapist who is there and yet "not there" is often needed to help untangle the symbolic feelings, images and thoughts that will of their own energy be spontaneously projected on one's blank mind screen. Here again, we see the potency in the contradiction of life. You must have
aloneness to experience oneself.

Let us quote Spinosa again, "Nothing can be understood in isolation." Therefore, there must also be at some point a sharing to gain understanding and verification of oneself. Through the process of beginning to experience oneself in aloneness and feeling one's ability to be self-sufficient in the world, one begins to establish the feeling of self-worth. Through unconditional love, one *receives* or is *given* a feeling of worth because one exists. Through the development of autonomy through aloneness, one begins to experience one's own personal existence and simultaneously begin to establish the feeling of self-worth.

This is in keeping with Piaget's Sensorimotor or first stage of cognitive development, wherein the child discovers relationships between its body and its environment. Piaget's theory highlights how this is the important period of separation of the self.

Perhaps you now begin to sense how it becomes necessary, as one approaches each new step of growth, that one must go back and refuel oneself by reworking all of the earlier steps. This inner conviction of continuity is critical for developing persons to confirm their sense of autonomous growth and appreciation for feelings.

Sexuality

The process of
becoming one with
oneself and one's
universe.

Chapter 6
Initiative versus Guilt

Synopsis:

Now with a sense of self-worth, the child feels the environment is its world and begins to explore his/her ability to interact with the world. A glow of pride radiates from each successful new experience. Autonomy fuels the freedom of going into the world and pride is the prerequisite for establishing initiative. The contradiction to initiative is guilt. The child who lacks a secure sense of worth or self-worth is vulnerable, feeling guilt when his/her attempts at initiative are met with don'ts or mustn'ts or guilt, provoking labels of "bad boy" or "bad girl."

Pride leads to the foundation for the feeling of responsibility. Not to accept responsibility for its initiation would diminish the child's feeling of pride. In contrast, with guilt we see the development of lying. The child herein needs to distance himself/herself from its "evil actions" and the fear of guilt and punishment.

At this stage, the child's energy flow is discovered to be primarily sexual in origin. My definition of sexuality is "the feeling that grows out of the process of a human being pridefully becoming one with oneself and one's universe." Issues of suppression, repression, sublimation, and the Oedipal Complex, with its resolution process of identification, are elucidated.

Let us move along bearing in mind the pyramid effect all preceding steps have upon the current one under study.

Assuming the child has had a bountiful degree of success achieving a sense of trust and autonomy, little by little the child increases its locomotion into the world, until it feels the environment to be its world. With a sense of security in its autonomy, the child begins on its own to explore its ability to interact with the world. What does the child feel as it climbs steps or a hill in the backyard and views the world from the new viewpoint it has created for itself? Imagine the child having picked a beautiful ripe tomato or flower from the garden, and further explores it by squeezing the tomato until seeds burst forth, or removing the flower petals until only the center remains. This is a significant moment that many people never fully appreciate. It is that supreme encompassing glow of pride that radiates from a child as it grasps each new feeling of having initiated a fresh experience in life for itself.

Pride is the feeling which feeds the freedom of going into the world, and is the prerequisite for the establishment of the character trait of initiative. This foundation of trust that one's needs can be met in the world, and a secure feeling of autonomy about one's ability to stand on one's own, naturally sets the stage for the need of initiative to arise.

Another intriguing concept may begin to assert itself. The successful fulfillment of the specific need in each step actually kindles the flame and, in a sense, demands one proceed with the work of the next step. This increase of momentum indicates there is no turning back on oneself.

We now need to appreciate in detail the contradictions of initiative. If the child has come this far with feelings of worthlessness and distrust that its needs can be met in the world, and doubts it can stand alone, its feeling of precariousness will dominate as it begins to explore the world. First, it will not feel the world, as *its world* because of its feelings of worthlessness, distrust and self-doubt. The world will be felt as belonging to others who have worth. The sensitive, young hand that picks and squeezes the flower may well be slapped, accompanied by expressions of "mustn't" or "bad girl" or "bad boy" or "good boys or girls don't hurt the pretty tomatoes or flowers."

Allen Schore's research of twelve years demonstrated that mothers of toddlers express a prohibition such as NO! or DON'T! with the all too often physical punishment on the average of every nine minutes. You can see how the contradiction to initiative, quilt, may be easily fostered, and how feelings of pride with desire for initiation of new learning experiences can be severely impaired.

Consider also how fear, which the child felt in the previous step during aloneness will now spread so it develops fears involving almost any conceivable activity of life. The manifold mysteries of life multiply geometrically. One of the most crucial needs for life and the development of civilization, the character trait of being responsible, *very subtly* begins to occur at this time.

As the child begins to feel pride in itself and a need to initiate new learning experiences, it glows in the realization that it is the one that fantasizes, deliberates, decides, and then carries through the initiation of the new experience. *Through pride, therefore, also lies the beginning foundation for responsibility,* Not to accept responsibility for its initiations would necessarily diminish the child's feeling of pride.

In Piaget's second or Preoperational Stage of cognitive development, this is a time of egocentrism or belief that everyone thinks as they do— that the world is created for them and they can control it. There is a belief that all things in life with a common denominator are identical, which leads to errors in classification. Intuitive thinking predominates from ages four through seven and includes the belief that nature, just like the self, is alive and controllable. Symbols are seen and felt to be directly created by human beings.

Now it is clearer how without pride—but with fear, guilt, and punishment—a child must learn to lie to attempt to separate itself as the causative force of its evil actions. Similarly, it cannot initiate and take for itself. Therefore, it learns to cheat and steal from others who are not evil and who have good or worth that it desires.

Just as subtly, the child who experiences itself as evil will also begin to experience how, after it goes through the required amount of anguish and suffering, it will be reaccepted and feel cleansed of its evil. It will *almost* feel it has earned worth. The worth, of course, is conditional on not repeating the evil. If that is the closest the child come to feeling worth or value, it is essentially inescapably trapped into repeating its evil act. This is certainly the basis for many facets of criminal recidivism.

This clearly exemplifies the concept of a repetition: compulsion. An attempt for a feeling of worth through a mechanism that cannot work—but it comes close—is repeated compulsively, endlessly. This is a beautiful example of the analytic balance between closeness and distance of the feeling of worth. The child will certainly still feel at distance from a true feeling of worth.

Look closely now at the pattern of behavior that begins to crystallize between the child and the punitive, then suddenly conditionally accepting parent. By repeating its evil act, the child learns it will be punished and suffer, but that its reward (a kind of acceptance) will follow. What a sense of power the child begins to realize it has through its experience of guilt. If the child suffers as demanded, the parent must then give recognition. The parent, of course, has contributed to this pattern by its attempt to control the child. The parent determines the goodness or evil of the child and achieves its own feeling of control.

Extend a little further and you will see the parent, in this example, as a version of the child with the strength to turn the tables. It is essentially still looking for its own sense of worth. This description of parent and child has the term neurotic interaction attached to it. It occurs nearly universally to some degree in relationships between people.

Guilt may be reconsidered as an attempt to gain a feeling of worth through utilizing the power of control or manipulation of another human being. Anyone who sets himself or herself up as the determiner of the value of another human being is only an extension of that person, still searching for a feeling of value. Perhaps the subtle interaction that flows from the mechanism of neurotic interaction has, and continues to have, the greatest effect of any principle on the course of civilization.

As described, the guilty child eventually becomes, in adulthood, the moralistic determining parent who then turns to inflicts the same process on its children repeat the same process on the next generation until the chain in broken. I call this process, *"the neurotic chain."* This unconsciously driven behavior gives justification to the lengthy, costly psychoanalytic treatment process.

Let us return to initiative through the feeling of pride. This is the most powerful of human phenomena. As the child more and more experiences the world by interacting with it, an awareness of powerful sensitivity and energy from within various parts of its body, takes over. Sight, sound, smell, taste and touch are its tools to explore and initiate, and great delight is taken in them. However, there is an even stronger feeling which can often block out and obliterate those senses.

Have you ever watched a child, totally engulfed in some activity, suddenly stop and instantly be taken over by an interest in its genitals? There seems little question that the most sensitive and powerful part of the body has become the genitals. Very quickly we observe this child bestow its greatest pride on its genitals. Of all things, the child most wants to know, understand, and begin to explore the world with its genitals. As the child's preoccupation takes hold again and again, one senses *this is the primary source of the child's energy flow.*

And so it will be from then on. Genitals are the instruments of a human's procreative ability, and the energy through which we enter the world.

Sexuality grows out of the process of a human being pridefully becoming one with itself and its universe. The essential feeling in sexuality is pride. The arrival of true sexuality is announced through the appearance of initiative. I am describing one's *personal* physical, mental, emotional, and spiritual sexual experiences as an attempt to unite oneself with the personal self and the universe.

It is crucial to differentiate one's *shared* sexual experience from one's *sexual* experience. Though we make many necessary preliminary steps, true shared sexuality can only occur in a mature intimate relationship that will be discussed in detail in a later chapter. All sexuality prior to that point must be seen as elaborations of one's personal sexuality. If this process is understood and one understands the need to strive for pride in one's sexuality—and how, through pride, originates responsibility— then childhood, teenage, and young adult sexuality can be understood as a dynamic process of one's evolving *personal* sexuality. No one is truly able to participate in shared sexuality until one's identity is secure, which includes one's personal sexuality. Early developmental attempts at sexuality are naturally centered on the self and we cannot realistically expect there to be any true sharing.

Consider the child burdened with feelings of worthlessness, distrust, self-doubt, and guilt. With little ability to feel pride in its sexuality—and instead feeling bad, evil and guilty—he/she begins to shut off the energy constantly flowing through every second of life asleep and awake. This process of shutting off feeling the flow of sexual energy is called repression.

The flow, of course, continues inside of us and goes on at a level outside of our conscious awareness. This is often called our subconscious mind or simply the "unconscious." Because sexuality is the primary source of energy in life, the degree to which we use repression to force that energy into the unconscious, determines the degree to which the activities we engage in during life are directed by energy from our unconscious, which is out of our conscious awareness and therefore outside of our normal conscious control.

Age 3 to 6 demonstrates the onset of another major phenomenon of childhood development, namely, dreaming. Most commonly the dreams are expressions of fears breaking through in the symbolic form of animals or monsters. The underlying feelings, typically sexual in origin, create significant contradictions. The contradiction to the "feeling of fear" is the "feeling of fascination." Hidden in the symbolism of dreams is fascination, most commonly sexual.

I need to also outline another major psychological principle that dreams demonstrate necessary to an understanding of how the mind physically and psychologically work together amazingly, and unbelievably.

The metaphor used in more than 40 years with patients has them visualize the brain as a movie camera switched on at birth. Recent research proves it occurs in utero. This camera is operating throughout life and captures on film everything each one of us experiences. In addition, this camera is connected to a movie projector which continuously operates 24 hours a day throughout our life. It projects its film to our own brain via our dreams, day-dreams, "moments of being spaced out," as well as in our conscious processes of reviewing, synthesizing, and deliberating throughout the day. The brain provides an opportunity to synthesize our experiences and work and rework the contradictions that occur continuously in our lives. The ability to formulate this synthesis into dreams becomes manifest at this developmental stage as a result of the pressure to suppress, repress, and sublimate to a high degree dealing with sexuality.

Brain research could determine the precursors that may occur prior to the developmental stage of dreaming and follow brain processes in sleep throughout childhood to help delineate developing disorders. Dream work by skilled professionals with children at this age could be crucial. Personally, I have found dream work, combined with art therapy or other physically expressive forms of therapy, helps to resolve childhood problems.

Now you can more clearly see why the feeling of responsibility emanating from pride is so enormously related to a free flow of sexuality. The destructiveness to society by organized religions, through the centuries, by its position on sexuality, is immeasurable. The unfortunate child, with guilt and its resultant inhibitions and restrictions, can again only stand back, observe those who exhibit pride in their sexuality, and imagine ways to obtain it from those who have it. The commonly called sexual perversions have their origin in these feelings.

Perhaps the example that society most abhors, because of its devastating effects, is the pedophile. Almost daily somewhere in the nation is another "Amber Alert" involving a missing child typically resulting in a sexual assault and/or homicide. Society is often unaware that for every act for which a pedophile is prosecuted dozens to hundreds of prior victims have been assaulted by that one individual.

Here is a dramatic example of an individual, deficient in his own sense of value, self-worth, and pride in his sexuality, unconsciously trying to incorporate this earliest sense of emerging pride in sexuality from an infant or child, or innocent victim. Almost universally at the outset of a pedophile's behavior, he claims to love children and tries to be loving and kind. Obviously, over time, these distortions increase and magnify, leading to all types of crime. The saga of the Michael Jackson case in 2005 is worthy of close study to understand more intimately the dynamics involved in complicated sexual identity development.

More profoundly helpful would be an in-depth study of sexually offending convicted priests. The serial rapist and murderer is a variation of this process with the addition of desire for control and an expression of rage so often directed at the sexual object as seen in serial prostitute killers. It would be most helpful if one could study in depth the BTK Wichita, Kan., serial murderer. "The Repetition Compulsion," as explained on page 41, is the underlying dynamic in the pedophile, the serial rapist, and serial murderer. We now understand and try more dynamically to describe these activities as attempts to achieve some feeling of pride in sexuality. Rarely does one see or feel pride emanating from people who utilize these activities as their major effort to achieve personal and or shared sexual satisfaction.

We can now return to the man who experienced feelings of jealousy and suspiciousness at the party with his wife. This man is insecure in the value or worth of his sexuality. At those moments, he is obviously not feeling pride in his sexuality. The feeling of jealousy of the apparent greater value of another man's sexuality in his wife's eyes is actually an awareness that what apparently is present and valuable in another man is potentially also present in himself. He simply as not realized it.

Jealousy is an awareness, through another, of what is inherently present but unrealized in oneself. Suspiciousness, or its more pronounced elaboration in paranoia, is a projection upon another person of what one desires to take from that person because of the perceived lack of oneself,

The child with its sexual energy freely and pridefully flowing can initiate new life experiences in a quite direct manner. The child burdened with guilt and its sexual energy repressed to its unconscious approaches life in a very different manner. Again, make no mistake that this sexual energy is a constant throughout life, and extremely powerful. He or she will use whatever means are available to gain expression using whatever disguises are necessary. The child begins to learn he or she is punished for some activities, he or she appears to be rewarded by the moralistic parent for other activities. Why not pour energies into the activities and appears to be that are rewarded?

Here then are the origins of behavior modification and how it capitalizes on the neurotic interaction process. Therefore, its ultimate effect on civilization is to perpetuate neurotic interaction, an ultimately destructive process. It denies the need for basic trust and autonomy.

Returning to the child, we essentially see that what the moralistic parent will reward is what the moralistic parent has had to borrow from some external element in the world, because this parent has no real feeling of worth from within itself. Here we begin to fully see the impact of societies and cultures on the individual. Because societies are made up of individuals, the position of a society on our scales of evolutionary human growth will naturally be determined by the forces of power going on within the individuals.[1]

Returning to the child and using our present American society as an example, it appears that *success* is the ongoing apparent good that has been most strongly fostered and rewarded. So here is where the child's repressed sexual energy can find a most easily and readily disguised current avenue of expression. The problem, however, is our unconscious knows the energy is sexual and the real desire is to be one with its world through sexuality. As the energy attaches to its current avenue of expression—success—it will again try to gain some direct expression of its sexual nature, which is forbidden as evil and threatens guilt and punishment.

The beginning attainment of success, recognized as essentially sexual by the unconscious, begins to call up fear that its true nature will be discovered or in some way break out directly.

If success remains—the apparent cultural evidence of value or goodness—this process like any "good neurotic process" must be repeated endlessly. President Nixon repeated the process nine times most prominently during Watergate when he had the largest electoral landslide vote in history.

The beautiful and tragic example of this in our present day I have named "The Nixon Neurosis" or "Success Neurosis" or "The Present Day American Cultural Neurosis."[25,26] Perhaps my patients will now also more clearly understand another equation: money, or power = sex. In fact, we could all benefit from studying it more closely.

---

1   I hesitate to use the concept of "where the majority of individuals in a society are at, will determine where the society is at" because our experience shows that the power in a society does not always seem to rest with the majority. There is a degree of truth that power ultimately rests with the majority from a position of duration but certainly not necessarily from moment to moment.

Consider the impact our educational system has had, and continues to have, on each of us and, essentially, on the course of civilization. Organized religion historically began using Sunday School for suppressing sexuality. This moves us to the educational system, Monday through Friday. Its essential function has always been the repression of sexuality. There is a correlation between the gradual discovery of sexuality, at an earlier age than previously thought, and how organized religion, through its thinly veiled disguise of education, developed kindergarten, then preschool and finally nursery school.

To more clearly understand the use of education as a tool of organized religion, I need to speak to why organized religion came into being. Essentially, as humans began to be one with themselves and their universe through the feeling of pride in sexuality, individuals in power found it necessary to destroy or blunt the feeling of freedom and individuality that accompanies a free flow of sexual energy. Fear of reprisal in eternal hell fire from an unseen god who put commandments on seen and touchable stone that outlawed sexuality kept the status quo in power. Organized religion ultimately is a form of politics. Political power is the neurotic substitute for the absence of healthy feelings of power in one's sexuality to become one with oneself and one's universe. It is not surprising how commonly politicians become destroyed by their sexual misadventures? How many children get to take out their genitals and play with them in preschool? Do you ever expect to see children publicly playing with each other's genitals in school rather than secretly with a sense of prohibition.

On Saturday Christian children had to line up in the afternoon in church for the mortifying experience of the confessional box. I can look back now with some amusement at how a sly contest went on to be the one to spend the shortest time in the box. The understanding of course, being that the amount of time taken depended on the number of and magnitude of one's misdeeds and sexual sins of the past week.

We have become marvelously adept devising new neurotic substitutes so there can be some outlet for our ever-present sexual energy. The most universally constant down through the ages has been games. Games also demonstrate how an essentially neurotic process eventually destroys itself. There is a rise and fall in popularity in every sporting event. Because certain events such as swimming, gymnastics, fencing, most closely allow sexual expression, they may never die. Dancing (a horizontal desire in a vertical position) will never end.

Transactional analysis is a current psychological game of popularity. It is a thinly veiled modification of the aversion techniques of behavior modification. Because women have finally begun to approach equality in the Olympic Games, could those hallowed games be also at risk? I found myself silently smiling through the latest Olympic games upon realizing that world politics, games, and sexuality were all clearly in the same arenas simultaneously.

I admit I am basically an optimist. On the positive side of the scales, one also sees the process of sublimation now begin to occur. Sublimation is an unconscious process by which repressed energy, essentially sexual, is converted into other activities more acceptable to the ego dictated by society's norms and dictates. Thus, one sees a major impetus to the process of performance and success-driven impulses.

Consider the child burdened with feelings of worthlessness, distrust, self-doubt, and guilt. In her quest for some measure of trust of value, autonomy, and pride in her ability to initiate, we have seen how she may become like a puppet manipulated by her parent or parents. "Like father, like son" is a common aphorism. How long have daughters trained and conditioned to earn the honor of being married in the wedding gown handed down through several generations with inherently implied strict moral attitudes. Have you honestly ever seen a mother who truly rejoiced in hoping or feeling that *her daughter* had surpassed herself in sexual happiness?

I owned a women's apparel shop at one time and shuddered whenever I had to endure a mother and daughter shopping together. Mothers would almost always try to steer their teenage daughters away from the most sexually stimulating attire. Bitter squabbles often erupted. Using reverse psychology with the mother often helped the young daughter leave the store quite happy. Mothers usually smirked at my male suggestions: that certain conservative clothing would be most attractive for their daughter. They, then would choose something more risque to demonstrate their superiority over me.

One can predict a phobic woman's mother and grandmother had identical phobias. However, at least one new additional phobia is added with each generation. Park Hill is an old, very close-knit area in Denver where late teenage or early adult women patients came into my practice. I was perplexed, amazed, and amused as I discovered all patients from that neighborhood were phobic with essentially mirror-image phobias.

I was taught that it was in the nature of phobias to spread, but this was truly almost beyond belief. In the most subtle manner conceivable, the child realizes this feeling originates within. The feeling, though pleasurable to experience alone, seems to invariably draw the child to a movement toward something or someone outside of itself. Remember: Sexuality grows out of the process of a human being pridefully becoming one with itself and its universe.

The more neurotic the child at age 3, the more he will neurotically identify with one or both parents. The more neurotic the identification, the less of a chance he will have of becoming a viable individual in life. Early in life it may appear a child will follow in a parent's footsteps. Everyone greatly predicts and awaits the child surpassing the parent in the parent's field, but it does not often happen! It is nearly impossible, because a law of diminishing effectiveness occurs in any neurotic process.

Now let us discuss one of the most singularly powerful developmental events in each of our lives. Consider this has been—and will be—the case throughout the history of human civilization.

The child who arrives at this point in life—with a relatively abundant measure of trust in his/her value, a solid sense of autonomy, and pride in his ability to initiate, and as well throbbing pulsations in his genitals—will discover a natural inner sense of being drawn to someone of the opposite sex. Playful curiosity will lead to natural experimentation with other children. A more intense feeling of need will naturally draw the child toward the most cherished adult of the opposite gender in his world, most typically a parent.

This attraction immediately creates the most overwhelming contradiction of the child's young life. For the girl to have her father in a loving sexual relationship or the boy to have his mother in a similar relationship, means having to face the dilemma of the special loving sexual relationship between the mother and father. Until this point, the child has dealt with life in relatively absolute black or white measurements.

Essentially he can only see that fulfilling his need must mean removing the opposite parent. The child knows the power of sexual feelings and can only infer it to be the same in the parent it needs to displace. The fear of potential rage from the displaced parent leads to the feeling that the only way to displace the parent securely means murder. What more powerful contradiction could possibly exist than to experience the need for a close loving sexual union that leads to murder. This example presents in the most ideal family situation, according to the child who is most filled with a bounteous flow of spontaneous energy. Again recall Hegel's quotation, "Something has vital force only when it contains contradiction."

This one event has a universal effect on human beings. Have you ever wondered why people essentially cannot recall much of their lives prior to 4 or 5 years of age? However, all parents believe a pre-

4-5 year-old's memory function to be an amazing phenomena. The reason is simply that this contradiction, the Oedipal Complex, is so overwhelmingly threatening that all prior memories and current conflict must be repressed. Remember that any repressed drive will forever attempt to gain consciousness and resolution.

Perhaps now you can get a feeling for the profound effect an unresolved Oedipus complex may have on individual humans and civilization.

It is time to gain a better appreciation of pride on the five balances scale. Illustrating the first balance of the moment versus duration, let us use the experience of the child fondling her genitals during one of those moments of throbbing pulsation. Each moment has its own special pride, ranging from overwhelming total body explosiveness to the slightest gentle tingling—and every conceivable sensation between the two. The child feels a sense of personal individual power. If she feels open and free to appreciate each new experience without guilt, the child will gradually realize the importance of personal pride and that tremendous feeling of internal energy for the duration of life.

Considering the second balance, each experience will be different within a broad range and yet the feeling of pride will have a sameness to it, especially as it relates to a sense of internal energy. Here a powerful yet barely perceptible force in life begins to reveal itself. On the third scale, as the child again and again experiences pride in her sexuality, she senses the closeness to totality or completeness, yet simultaneously retains a sense of distance from that completeness. In the most subtle manner conceivable, the child realizes that although this feeling originates from within the self, the feeling, though pleasurable to experience alone, seems invariably to draw the child toward something or someone outside the self. Sexuality is the feeling that grows from the process of a human being pridefully becoming one with his/herself and the universe.

Moving to the fourth balance, we see the child beginning to use its pride through sexuality to find union with its universe. Specifically, the child will experiment in every conceivable way to masturbate with every available object and/or person in its universe in its attempt for union with its universe. Here we find a healthy evolutionary growth process. We gain an understanding of all types of fetishes, exhibitionism, pedaphobia, voyeurism, bestiality, incest, nymphomania, and on and on.

Again, if you appreciate my definition of sexuality, you understand how all of these experiences can be a natural part of life. Of course, one can become "neurotically or psychotically hung up" and fail to continue to grow in life. In each instance, the child may have some feeling and moment of union with the particular person or object in its universe, but there will always be the recurring awareness of its separateness.

This brings us to the fifth balance. With each experience comes increased feelings of knowing oneself, a totality of oneself, and being one with one's universe. However, as the experience winds down, there will be the ever-recurring awareness there is still something missing and not known.

What we desire for the child is a home where the parent or parents are clear about the priority of their own personal sexual needs, which would help the child realize that sexual needs do not find natural total fulfillment in parents. The child, nonetheless, continues to feel pride in its sexuality from within itself and from the radiation of that feeling in the parent for itself and for its child. This mutual feeling of pride and respect between parent and child in one's own and each other's individual sexuality forms the basis of healthy identification.

The process of healthy identification is the basis for the resolution of the Oedipal Complex.

Finally, I will describe the anticipated or predictable physical misfortunes awaiting those of us who fail to grow through this period with reasonable success.

Sexual frigidity would certainly be prominent and as a corollary.

We might see all the previously mentioned forms of sexuality alone or in combination retained compulsively. Because of the emergence of repression at this point in life, repressed sexual energy must attempt to gain consciousness in some disguised manner, so we can see malfunction develop in any organ or function of the body. The power of sexuality is enormous and leads to every possible *conversion reaction* imaginable. Conversion reaction describes how repressed sexual energy is converted into some altered physical function of the body. Paralysis of an arm or leg or blindness that has no physical basis were once some of the more common examples before our society, in general, became too sophisticated to allow ourselves to use such easily detected "hysterical symptoms."

Our unconscious always keeps abreast of the times. Now we find much more sophisticated and often slyly ingenious conversion reactions that can, at times, require dozens of tests and thousands of dollars of expert medical consultation and millions of dollars of the latest, most sophisticated equipment to determine that these symptoms are not organically founded. Needless to say, the patient may die, get lost in a medical maze, or get frustrated and quit—that is, if the physician doesn't get to that point first.

On Developing the Freedom of Initiative

On a deeper level, the concept implies there must be an internal *source of energy* that is set in motion. The concept of initiative also implies setting the energy in motion must also come from within—that it, in effect, must be self-starting, or self-igniting. Sexuality is the internal energy source that must be set in motion for true initiative to occur. We can now deduce that masturbation is the essential need or step required for the development of initiative. Natural, spontaneous, comfortable, *prideful* masturbation will result in an outpouring of energy in many directions. The direction is simple; the accomplishment, often extremely difficult.

Perhaps what we now need is a book on the joys of masturbation and a movie for children on the same subject.

There is clearly a need for the solid core of worth through unconditional love and for self-worth through autonomy before one is likely to see comfortable experimentation with masturbation. The position of society can make this task enormously difficult.

Total body awareness is extremely vital and I feel should be the primary endeavor of nursery schools. It would immensely enhance learning capabilities for the rest of one's life. I find it is particularly difficult for people trapped in a neurosis to see the importance in this step. There almost is invariably a difficulty in the two earlier, which must be worked through sufficiently before progress can be made via masturbation.

The importance of accomplishing necessary work correcting our deficiencies in life in a specific, appropriate, logical, orderly fashion can best be appreciated. Because of the intensity of our sexual feelings, they can often lead to an incorrect application. I specifically mean masturbation can often temporarily discharge tension and *we may try to accomplish the task of autonomy or other steps* by its mistaken usage. Pride can be the key to help us know or verify with ourselves that we are on target with masturbation. There will begin to be an interest and curiosity, not only of oneself, but more important with the sexuality of others about us. This promotes a natural progression to our next step of expansiveness.

A playmate
is the
absolute
requirement of
childhood.

Chapter 7
Expansiveness versus Inferiority

Synopsis:

A child well blessed in the first three stages will figuratively explode with inquisitiveness about the universe. Fun is the *de rigeur* of expansiveness with inferiority its contradiction. The need for a playmate to share expansiveness is an outgrowth of Spinosa's quotation "Nothing can be understood in isolation."

Current issues concerning new studies of how the universe is rapidly changing, the enormous new sources of knowledge available through the internet, and the current epidemic of ADD and ADHD are discussed.

One should sense how a child, who has evolved to this point with a wealth of trust, autonomy, and pride would be in the position of naturally experiencing great pleasure in an ever-increasing scope of the world. Indeed, there is once again that need to push on, to grow and become more and more one with the universe. A child thus blessed will have a great experience in inquisitiveness about the universe. We are often amazed by how there is seemingly no limit to what a child of ages 6-12 wants to know about life and the universe. This is truly a time of expansiveness for a solidly evolving child.

If we closely observe a child who has acquired a considerable sense of distrust, self-doubt, and guilt, we begin to see a continuing process of withdrawal, lack of initiative, and the contradictory feeling of inferiority in view of itself in relationship to the universe.

The most obvious consistent quality present on the face of a child involved in zooming expansive inquisitiveness is fun. Fun is the *de rigeur* of expansiveness. The child seeking knowledge at this point will find fun doing many, many things. In fact, it could be stated that, as a rule, if it's not fun, it's not worth doing. Please don't be confused into the false belief that for something to be fun it necessarily implies that it is easy or it does not require effort. Children often expend vast amounts of energy building mud or dirt castles, taking apart toys (and even reassembling them), or dressing and grooming dolls.

I recall seeing children of this age standing in front of mirrors at fun houses. We would do well, periodically in life, to return to that experience in a meaningful way. In this experience, one can graphically see the difference between a child whose inner experience is of expansiveness and the child whose major internal experience is of inferiority. The latter child standing in front of the distorting mirrors will likely be critical of itself, may even be frightened or bolt away, and will have little if any experience of "fun" feelings.

Who could question that the breadth of one's life experiences will be profoundly influenced by the child's experiences at this step in its process of evolutionary development? I have found children who often do well in the first one to three years of school, may begin to shut down, regress, and seem to unlearn much of what was initially interesting, challenging, and fun. After very close, in-depth research of youngsters who exhibited these characteristics, by focusing on their feelings of that era, I have repeatedly been appalled by the discovery that these children became bored. The limitations, restrictions, rigidity of our society—particularly as dominated by religious and educational institutions and by the initiation of the "confession of guilt for sins" that begins at this era (naturally, the timing is excellent)—successfully blows out the candle of "fun" and the desire for expansiveness in many children. The least we do as a society is to diligently weave a good-sized bushel basket to cover the flame of inquisitiveness in our children.

Often we even perceive the child withdrawing due to feelings of inferiority as being quite noble for such early development , and we label it humility. It is true we may also see a child struggle to maintain its drive for expansiveness and begin to develop the attitude of superiority, always needing to be the best, or "lord it over" the other children. It is important to appreciate the feeling of expansiveness is primarily an internal feeling that the child experiences while becoming more and more one with its universe. Most of the energy that propels this inquisitiveness and subsequent expansiveness is sexual in origin.

As I described in the preceding chapter, the child has learned how vital the need is to develop and create a personal world to be healthy and no longer remain dependent or to seek its major gratification with a parent. You may appreciate why we see very little overt open sexuality at this period. Because the child needs to explore, discover, create, and develop a world of its own, the child intently develops wide and deep feelings and acquire knowledge of life and the world. This must occur before the child can again go through the more direct sexual process of becoming one with its new self-discovered and created universe.

The child who is in difficulty will find it increasingly tough to contain all of its repressed and suppressed energy. Eventually, this energy must be released in hyperactivity, delinquency, withdrawal and depression, or increasingly limiting forms of physical ailments.

At this time in life the child enters into one of the most difficult-to-understand arenas of our existence. Recall my metaphor of dropping the pebble into water and attempting to come to an intimate knowledge of all that occurs. To this point, we have primarily been attempting to study the pebble and know its nature and, to some extent, the forces of the water into which it has been dropped. Now we, just as the child, need to better understand the world outside of us, as well as our inner personal world.

Only since the human race has come to appreciate the risks that have been placed on the environment, have we begun to make *determined* efforts to understand our surprisingly fragile environment. Just as the two-year-old pulls off the petals of the flower, and the three-year-old demolishes a toy trying to get an awareness of the inner essence of those things, the 6-12-year-old must struggle to grasp the essential forces the universe will exert on its life, and vice versa. To accomplish this, there occurs the gentle realization that one needs to know and understand botany, physics, chemistry, astronomy, the earth sciences, and, most of all, mathematics. Ultimately, one must come to a *knowledge of the essence of the universe.*

Fortunately, Piaget's third or Concrete Operational Stage of cognitive development beautifully cooperates with this process. There is a beginning ability to reason logically, organize thoughts and actual objects in a concrete manner. Inductive logic, going from specific examples to a general principle, rules this period—as opposed to deductive logic that goes from general principles to a specific. Abstract reasoning does not develop until late preteenage development.

I have found great impetus trying to integrate the philosophy of Hegel and the works of Freud with unconscious repression, including psychosexual development and Einstein, who stands alone as the man who grasped the need to put it all together and make it understandable.

If philosophy by definition is the synthesis of all knowledge in a unifiable, knowledgeable whole, then Einstein was the world's greatest philosopher to date. But he made a very difficult choice to specialize in the one area he felt most vital. Indeed Einstein admitted that his greatest insights originated intuitively from within rather than out of the multitudes of facts he assembled. The analytical balances we use are elaborations of his theory of relativity.

I have the nagging feeling that a disproof of a portion of the Theory of Relativity is suggested in the system presented in this book, where there is always possible room for further elaboration or continued growth of human experience. I am speaking specifically to the concept of the speed of light in a vacuum as being a fixed, maximum velocity. I propose more specifically, that there must be a homogeneous nature to the laws that govern the physical universe, as well as those that govern our affectual universe.

Recall my statement early in the chapter on human need regarding the feeling that we may go on and on forever. See how important the stage of expansiveness really is? I cannot help but wonder how things might proceed if philosophy was the core of learning at ages 6-12. Our society still suffers from a widespread lack of critical thinking, despite supposed improvements in our educational system and elaborate and technically sophisticated learning tools (computers, etc.) and progressive classroom design.

I use the example of a child (or children, since true group play or fun evolves at this point) building a sand castle at the oceanside. Each moment the child molds the moist sand can give the experience of the growth or expansion of the formed object and the fun of each moment's experience can go on for hours. If you have ever built sand castles, recall it. The fun endures because for those moments you were very intimately being one with your universe, personally giving it a unique shape. The delightful experience of crawling inside your sand castle will capture your sense of unity with the feeling of fun.

Nonetheless, you and the sand castle and the feeling of fun have separate existences. The feeling of fun will also be different as you stand at a distance from it, and when you are very close to it putting it into various shapes and forms. The entire fun experience of building the sand castle will have a certain even sameness, yet each moment and arrangement will bring different smiles and fun feelings. Your feeling of fun will feel complete at moments. Yet the awareness that your castle will disappear may trouble you with doubt.

Do you really know the feeling of fun you are experiencing? If you (or you and your family) have yet to built a sand castle, don't let your days become too numbered before you experience it. One of the amazing wonders of our physical universe you can share is the discovery that each grain of sand is encapsulated in its own drop of water. I have believed for most of my life that if you can, as a child, directly experience building a sand castle, important imprinting occurs that will assist immeasurably in the next stage of evolutionary growth.

During this stage of development, the physical growth process of the child is as important in many ways as the mental development in all the stages. The contradiction that goes on naturally between growth and the process of developing physical coordination can be a major struggle in itself, requiring abundant energy devoted; however, not excessive to the degree of obsession. Yoga could be very successfully introduced to the child at this time.

On Becoming Expansive

There is something ironically amusing writing about how one is to go about having fun. From a rather intellectual viewpoint, the energy and pleasure that took its root in our emerging personal sexuality has its natural progression and expression in "fun with all aspects of life". During this period of growth, the world can appear to be a wonderful and pleasurable personal adventure. From this perspective one can more easily understand how the vast majority of energy for life's activities has its roots in sexuality.

At this stage of development, the only means by which more fun and expansiveness can occur is to find a playmate! Again Spinosa's quote of "Nothing can be understood in isolation," holds true. Because we are speaking of an enormous expansiveness in learning and becoming one with one's universe, we need another being with whom to share and verify our discoveries.

There is also another very vital dynamic that becomes prominent at this point. Whereas it was vital and important in the previous step to be often deeply engrossed in one's own sexuality personally and exclusively, it now becomes vital that the enormous energy now manifested be able to expand and grow to include others. In this stage, the sexual energy is necessarily sublimated into many diverse activities that are nongenital or not overtly sexual to learn as much as possible about our universe and our intimate relationship with it.

However, the playmate is vital because there must be some sharing with another human being, including at times some of the genital, physiological energy, even if it occurs in a sublimated playful fun posture. If this sharing does not occur, what we begin to see is an internalized hyperactivity from the contained energy, or the initialization of patterns of increased body awareness and sensitivity leading to the origins of hypochondriasis, because all the sexual energy is focused on the self.

One of the vital needs in the relationship of playmates is that there be a mutuality of the ability to initiate playfulness and fun activities. There is a natural need to retouch and rework feelings of trust, autonomy, and initiative with *oneself and one's playmate.* Engaging in fun activities with that playmate ultimately leads to throwing open the doors of the world, experiencing much of the world in new ways where each nuance and texture can be appreciated with amazement and delight. *Both playmates* must have sufficiently accomplished the work of the first 3 steps individually and then must accomplish those steps together in their relationship, if there is to be true expansiveness. Clearly, a number of trials and errors may occur before the playmates discover one another and establish this crucial and delightful relationship. It is also essential to realize all of what I have said here applies to having playmates of both sexes. One cannot have a full awareness, appreciation, and knowledge of one's universe unless it includes viewpoints from both sexual poles.

A Definition of Emotional Illness

The lack of fulfillment of our God-given talents which leads to two mandates in choosing a life career.

1. If it ain't fun, it ain't worth it.
(Doing What Comes Naturally)

2. It should be as easy as falling off a log.

Chapter 8
Identity versus Diffusion

Synopsis:

I propose adolescence begins the era of questioning *who am I?* and *where do I fit into the grand design of the universe?* In addition, a physiological and a psychological explosion occurs with an awareness of one's sexual drive and a natural attraction to the sexuality of others.

The ultimate requirement of Identity centers on a focus and specificity. The relationship of our specific Identity to the growth process of the universe is discussed. The contradiction to Identity is Diffusion, which often occurs in those who have been relatively unsuccessful in the prior stages of development. The re-emergence of responsibility gradually occurs as a young person realizes only he/she can hold the keys to the fulfillment of one's personal needs in the long haul of life.

"Process is Content" describes the way Identity originates, via experiencing the entire process, seeing things to their end, while maintaining focus, specificity, and patience.

The most natural phenomenon transpires as the child, who has been going through an enormous period of expansiveness learning and becoming one with its universe, begins to be plagued by questions: Who am I? What am I? Where do I fit in the grand design of this beautiful and complex universe? There is a sense that something purposeful and meaningful needs to come out of one's life. Though it has been building gradually for sometime, there is the explosive awareness of the opposite sex and one's own sexual physiology.

Adolescence can best perhaps be described metaphorically, if we compare it to the past seven decades since World War II. Indeed, we might say that our earth is going through adolescence, if we view it as a human entity, which I believe more and more is the truth. I propose the cultural groups of nations and world society must follow the same essential developmental: evolutionary growth process as our individual child. Having surveyed all the countries of the world, I feel one can discern where a nation is in its human evolutionary growth process and one can also predict the struggles it will face in the near future.

I strongly urge the reader to review *A New Synthesis of Evolution,* by Teilhard De Chardin, Chapter III. He described the "within" of cosmic matter: *If the essence of Humanness is growth, then it follows that "growth" will be present as a driving intrinsic force in all that involves a human being.* As Spinosa stated, "Nothing can be understood in isolation." This principle underlies one of the essential characteristics of humans: human beings by nature are gregarious. Our Human social cultural groups will therefore be internally propelled by the same essence of growth as is every individual.

Our world society has been evolving at an explosive pace for the last 50 years and struggling with its identity. Adolescence in the individual is a period of explosive evolvement in a short period of time compared to the duration of a human existence. During this time, the adolescent must go through the struggle to achieve identity.

Consider carefully the meaning of identity. It brings total life's energy as a human being into focus. Can you imagine a time when all human beings who have ever been created will be in tune with our own special *specific* identity, which would put us in a balance with our physical universe? No doubt this viewpoint should leave sufficient room for all of us to maintain expansive personal growth!

It is now readily apparent that the ultimate requirement of identity is to be specific or to have *specificity.* Its contradiction is diffusion. We can have a greater sense of the importance of both contradictory forces at this stage of growth than at any other stage. It is vital there be a force that pushes us toward diffusion at this period of life. Through it, we are forced to search far and wide, in varied corners before bringing our energy into focus in a specific identity. We are also awakened to the fact that throughout our human existence we will be periodically required to reopen ourselves to some diffusion to refine our identity as our physical, human, and spiritual universe continues evolving.

We may now appreciate the subtle manner in which the propelling force of expansiveness in the preceding stage indirectly evolves into the "contradictory side of the coin" force of diffusion. If you carefully review the first four stages, this principle was in process from the beginning, Students of the human brain will now better understand the why; of how the brain evolved its capability for contralateral take-over of many functions and understand that this capability will evolve and expand as we evolve affectually as human beings.

At age 15 all parts of the brain, other than the prefrontals, myelinate, or stabilize, making permanent all brain developments that have been achieved up to that time. Because the secondary stage of prefrontal brain growth, beginning at age 15, is the highest evolutionary movement within us, it is the most fragile. This means the emotional nurturing received at this mid-teenage period serves as a determinant in the success or failure of this latest opening of intelligence. Therefore, parental and teacher positive nurturing support remain critical throughout adolescence, despite the adolescent's frequent involvement in rebellion regarding social acceptance.

The most exquisite mystery of how the physical universe, including our human physical body, stands ready and adaptably waiting for us to achieve a greater level of affectual growth begins to clarify itself at this point. It is so that it, too, may push on with its evolvement.

Further, we now get a most important understanding of how our specific identity does have a purposeful effect on our physical universe, and how each of our identities is essential to the overall evolutionary growth of our physical universe. How glorious it is that the Italians demand of their operatic performers, "Do it over until you do it right!" We need to realize creation demands the same of each of us. *Find your identity and fill it correctly. You will live your life over until you do. Our entire universe depends and waits on you.* There is a meaning and purpose in each of us!

Let us return to the source of our energy, which emanates out of our sexuality. Through the period of expansiveness, our sexual energy was learning about our universe. But now it must return to be a most powerful personal experience in each of us. Great people have invariably drawn great strength out of their sexuality. The enormous vitality that is born out of contradiction can be best appreciated studying woman and man. No greater symphony will ever be written than the one created when man and woman are able to unite together in joyous ecstasy. For that to happen, each one must first become that special individual that awaits within.

To begin the work of adolescence, there must first be a process of separating oneself from the enforced patterns, beliefs, and values of parents and society to make one's own personal assessment of what will be meaningful and fulfilling. At the same moment, we see the curious phenomena of adolescents fusing into the most cohesive of all observable groups, and whose allegiance to one another is often more dedicated than the sworn oaths of Mafioso families. A group identity in music, clothing, and social cliques serves as a vital transitional identity and a support against social rejection.

We might also observe that just as our world society appears to be in its adolescence, some nations are lagging behind while others are more advanced. Many people of the world are finally reaching this stage regardless of their chronological age. In the United States, it takes a man at least 40 years to reach this stage—if he ever does—and women seem to require about 30 years. Gail Sheehy's book, *Passages,* essentially describes the identity crisis that hits people in mid-life, 35-45 years of age.

A crucial premise carefully established throughout this book is that one must sufficiently complete the work of each stage of evolutionary development before one can reasonably begin fruitful work on the next stage. *One cannot skip any steps* and make significant progress in one's evolutionary growth. The colloquial expression of "being hung up" and "needing to get it all together" intuitively get to the truth of human evolutionary growth.

There is perhaps no greater level of risk involved than at the stage of identity vs. diffusion. Because one must split (at least temporarily) from parent's and societies' values and morals to have sufficient freedom to discover oneself, there is great risk of rejection and retaliation from the value-and-moral-setting neurotic society that still exists and experiences jealousy and revenge toward anyone daring enough to have a separate identity.

It is a function of uncovering and discovering one's identity that also demands a beginning search for a feeling of a home, roots.

One of the most powerful of all movements defining who and what we are, to advance toward crystallization as result of achieving a sense of identity, is we determine what the major and significant needs of our life will be. Underneath these decisions and choices lies that vital quality of life called responsibility. In the chapter on initiative, we learned responsibility can only arise out of taking pride in the initiation.

At the early point in life where initiative began, we could still justifiably expect many of our needs in life would be met by others and we could hold others outside of ourselves responsible for the fulfillment of our needs. At the point of achieving identity, however, there is a dramatic shift. The realization begins to unfold that if we wish to insist on defining who and what we are and wish to be, *only we personally can be responsible for the fulfilment of our needs and their attainment or lack of attainment.*

There is, therefore, an enormous sense of separateness or aloneness that, at some point, will begin to set in. This difficult conflict over a need for identity and the degree of separateness it necessitates—as well as the desire for sharing through our physically and emotionally blossoming sexuality (which I earlier defined as becoming one with oneself and our universe)—pushes the fragile adolescent, who has had poor or little success in all the previous stages of evolutionary growth, into overt psychosis of schizophrenia or manic depression.

On Attaining Identity

If there is a true pivotal point in life for nearly all people of the 20th century, it is the search for identity. Until this point in history, identity had not been of great importance to the vast majority of people. In fact, it had perhaps been of more value to the majority prior to the 20th century to not have an identity, Certainly, life for most went more easily and smoothly, if they did not engage in such a struggle. Religion and most nations preferred their people docile as "lambs" going contentedly as a "flock" behind their leaders. With the great world wars of the previous century, it became necessary for all women and men to be equally self-sufficient, autonomous, and productive to the point that in the modern western world one cannot make it without an identity.

The need to find purpose and meaning has become paramount. It has opened the doors to what is, for many, a very difficult struggle. Again, the difficulty of the struggle is dependent on how relatively well one has completed the work of the four preceding steps. Each succeeding step becomes somewhat more complex and requires a reworking and incorporation of the previous processes into the significant step at hand.

The most vital process in finding one's identity is *seeing something through to the end of its entire process.* Now my earlier statement that process is content has more solid meaning. One's identity can only come to realization by going through the process with focus, specificity, and patience.

One must incorporate, at times receiving unconditional love, being autonomous, feeling the pride of one's sexual energy at work, experiencing fun with others in the endeavor, and determining to see it through all the way. At the completion of this stage, one will know the process and the self are truly one.

There begins to arise at these moments, a need for a deeper feeling of sharing than that which occurred with one's playmate(s) during the process of expansiveness. This leads to the next chapter. Establishing and crystallizing one's identity is also an important factor in the development of courage. Unless one knows who one is and the meaning of one's existence within the universe, one rarely dares great risk because one does not have the courage that arises out of identity.

On Relationships

First, two individuals
must become,
and always remain,
their own person.

Then they may become
a couple.

Chapter 9
Intimacy versus Isolation

Synopsis:

Intimacy requires two individuals with fairly well-established identities willing to establish Openness. Intimacy occurs when two individuals simultaneously occupy the same-feeling space for a moment in time. All we have to truly share is our Identity. Intimacy requires each person to relinquish a degree of one's personal Identity to assume a portion of the other individual's Identity. A "new third space" then evolves, consisting of portions of the two separate Identities. It requires an ability to relinquish one's reality boundaries to experience genuinely shared sexuality, as opposed to personal sexuality.

The contradiction to Intimacy is Isolation, which most often occurs after unfulfilling attempts at Intimacy or after the loss of an intimate relationship.

*

People are creatures of habit, and because doctors (even psychiatrists!) are people, too, it should not surprise anyone to discover that after treating patients for more than fifteen years, I had developed some habitual phrases. The *useful* ones I found myself using most frequently were "First you become a person, then you become a couple" and "First you feel, then you know."

As I discussed in the previous chapter, for someone to have an identity, yet unable to share this identity or its fruits, would strike that person as meaningless. An often easily overlooked requirement for achieving intimacy is *two people*. Two people, with fairly well-established identities, who *desire* and are willing to work to establish *openness* (a rather pivotal precondition) are necessary.

The late preteenage years of eleven to twelve again see the emergence of Piaget's fourth or Formal Operational Stage of cognitive development. With the development of the ability for abstract reasoning and deductive logic, going from general principles to a specific, one can formulate hypotheses (i.e., this is a person capable of openness) and then test them out. This process is crucial going through the struggle for openness and ultimately achieving intimacy.

Only from a position of openness can sharing occur. Essentially, one shares qualities of oneself developed or discovered establishing one's identity. The only thing we can share is ourselves! Just as it can be most difficult to discover and establish one's identity, undoubtedly there can be great labor and, at times, deep emotional pain pursuing intimacy. Until we have a good grasp of the nature of genuine openness, we can deceive ourselves about its presence or lack of presence in others, as well as our own readiness for it. It is not easy to risk the full emotional exposure (or even physical exposure) of oneself. If it were that simple, perhaps we could eventually agree on some consistent behavioral norms. But it is not that simple! Each step of growth becomes a bit more difficult, not easier.

I define intimacy as "a sharing of oneself that occurs simultaneously between two people." Two people literally occupy the same feeling-space for a moment in time. This creates a contradiction that makes the achievement of intimacy a very rare occurrence in life. I have said that all we have to share in a real way is our identity. In intimacy, two people attempt to share their separate identities for a moment simultaneously. This requires that each person must *give up a degree* of one's personal identity to take in a portion of the other's identity and vice-versa. A new *third space* evolves that is made up of portions of the two separate identities. This ability to give up one's reality boundaries enables us to experience true shared sexuality, which we have differentiated from personal sexuality.

Giving up parts of one's identity or giving up part of one's ego boundary is, to a degree, what occurs in a person undergoing a psychotic process. This is no doubt why intimacy has a certain frightening quality to it, as well as the feeling of desire. Because of the fearful qualities in striving for intimacy, we see many people adopt the contradiction of intimacy, which is *isolation.* Two contradictory, yet insightful quotations deserve careful consideration at this point. Spinosa's "Nothing can be understood in isolation," and "Life is first, last, and always a singular journey," which I coined.

We can again appreciate Hegel's statement, "Something has vital force only when it contains contradiction. It is a measure of that force that the contradiction can be grasped and endured." For those familiar with Eastern philosophy, the symbol of the yin and yang opposites within a circle representing the Tao or natural principle of equilibrium is an apt representation of this concept, no more appropriate than in the context of human relationships.

After each moment of intimacy, there is the necessity for the two people to leave the new third space and return to their separate space or identity. Thus, there is the need for the contradictory feeling of isolation. In this momentary state of interdependency of the two contradictory forces of intimacy and isolation, one has the strongest sense of the truth of one's own existence and how each of these tidal forces contributes to a vast personal potential vitality. Isolation, of course, can become a defensive shelter from where some people do not emerge. This, naturally, most often occurs following a painful nonfulfilling attempt at intimacy or after the loss of an intimate relationship.

A force that amplifies this move toward isolation is the loss of personal power or self-esteem that results from a failure to achieve or maintain the intimate bond. Therefore, another contradictory conclusion can be reached, which is that individual personal power grows in proportion to the ability of the individual to achieve and maintain intimate relationships with others. Personal power is enhanced and fulfilled by sharing.

The position of empathy from which a therapist attempts to work is essentially a variation of intimacy in that the therapist attempts to enter the patient's identity or space with objectivity, but without the need to share personal identity with the patient.

Intimacy, which arises out of the sharing process, brings with it one of the most truly happy, peaceful feelings of human life, because for those moments we overcome our feelings of separateness, which Eric Fromm has pointed out is the root of all human anxiety.

One of the vital facets of people who have matured to achieve true intimacy is a constant feeling of curiosity about everything in their universe. To be able to share in the openness offered by others desiring intimacy, there is a need for openness to all areas of the physical, emotional, intellectual, and spiritual universe. The dynamic flow of energy in such individuals is easily felt, if it is worn comfortably, even peacefully, yet energetically. This state of casual dynamics is an outgrowth of considerable emotional involvement and not neurotic hyperactivity. People in this state appear healthy, radiant, and well adjusted. They are attractive, and people naturally enjoy their presence because it promotes good feeling, positive energy, and active accomplishment. It is highly contagious.

On Achieving Intimacy

It becomes more and more difficult to single out a specific process one must go through to attain these progressive qualities in life. However, if we carefully consider the idea of attempting to take in another person's identity and give a part of ourselves to another simultaneously, there is a particular quality that is crucial. Both people must have a total concentration on oneself and on each other. They must be very sensitive to themselves and to each other. Each must attain a heightened state of self-sensitivity, yet achieve an equal degree of perception directed with total concentration on the other person, so nothing is missed.

The crucial point is intimacy requires the two people to focus on the immediate moment. Intimacy requires living in the present, here and now. Each must have the ability to listen, to sense the *vibrations* of one's own feelings. Each cannot be distracted by anything else. The development of autonomy through aloneness is essential when one struggles with intimacy. We may also realize the new subtle interplay of forces mentioned previously in expansiveness.

For intimacy to occur, it requires two people to have each separately gone through all the previous steps of growth. They must also in their relationship have already gone through the steps of trust, autonomy, initiative, expansiveness, and identity before they can hope to tackle the work of intimacy.

One then realizes how gradually, subtly, the two people have developed their new *third space* in which they can have momentary periods of fusion. Essentially, one develops the ability for total concentration. Concentration is a gradual process strengthened during of each new step from autonomy onward. We must put it to its greatest test to date. Courage and risk-taking are vital. They underscore the absolute necessity of a good sense of identity as a prerequisite for intimacy.

One of the most common origins of the neurotic drive to know, to do, to be busy in speech, or activity is our "old friend," the success neurosis. This state is bound to sexual energy that has either been repressed or had to be repressed. For those fortunate people who reach this stage of development, they are most often optimistic, progressive, and often driven. They feel, in time, there may be a possibility of sharing with such openness. Those who develop a mature outlook realize that not everything desired can be attained immediately, especially true intimacy.

Generativity
occurs when identity
becomes an active, vital,
moving force
linked with infinity.

Chapter 10
Generativity versus Apathy

Synopsis:

Generativity is an active vital moving force that develops from within a person to manifest one's true Identity. Personal Growth is the feeling at the base of Generativity and ultimately requires the ability to relinquish conscious reality of the moment and focus on the universe in its totality.

A mature intimate relationship to provide strength when needed is a necessity to withstand the potential movement toward isolation, personal diminution, loss of Generativity, and the development of its contradiction, Apathy.

The need to become objective about one's abilities, talents, energy, and motivations in relationship to the universe will help one come to grips with the realization that we can only be who we are. Humility is the manifest evidence that one has become objective about oneself. This process was initiated while achieving Intimacy by knowing oneself through a partner's eyes, and through awareness and knowledge.

*

After delving into the issue of intimacy and the new shared third relationship, the stage is set for a discussion of generativity. In this context, generativity is an active vital moving force developed within a person. It is the manifesting one's being, the ideas one has discovered, and one's genuine identity. This stage does not necessarily mean a person is engaged in voluminous production or vast creativity, although that too lies in the realm of possibility. More than that, such a person intrinsically experiences an evolution, the absolute cornerstones of humanness.

Personal growth is the base of generativity. So few individuals, relatively speaking, make it to this point in life, and only one cultural group in the history of civilization of our world society, the Jews, has endured such a long difficult struggle.

Periods of regression occur in the lives of individuals, as in the history of nations to complicate and delay progress. One must always withhold judgement until the conclusion of such an evolvement, because one cannot always know these specific setbacks, challenges, and obstacles essential for the enrichment of character, maturity, creativity, and attainment of an individual or a culture in the future.

A recognizable example in history is the Renaissance which evolved from the grim adversity and plague-ridden horrors of the Dark Ages. Although it would be simplistic and indefensible to assert that the Renaissance could not have occurred without the torments of the Dark Ages, one cannot know for certain which elements may or may not have been essential ingredients. Perhaps such vitality, genius, and character are the products of adversity, and a less painful path was unavailable. As with all personal human struggles, one can never know for certain which periods of adversity are critical to one's later personal fulfillment and development.

One generative individual who remains prominent like an airport runway beacon at night is James Michener. His work underwent a constant process of evolutionary growth. With each new major work from this author, one saw a growth in breadth and depth. One might read his works in chronological order to appreciate this development and anticipate each succeeding work.

If individuals fail to reach a clear-cut identity or remain diffused and drift into isolation, the individual can easily develop a pattern of apathy as the contradiction to generativity.

In generativity, one most beautifully and profoundly sees the effect of the relative success of the preceding feeling of intimacy. At this point of development, one is dealing with a fairly small minority of people who have inhabited the earth. I avoid using the word creative until Section Three of the book titled "A Spiritual Universe: The Creative Being," because further evolutionary steps will be necessary. At this point we have the ability to generate but not create. Nonetheless, an individual who reaches this level of evolution is indeed a unique person.

A preliminary peak of secondary prefrontal brain growth occurs at age 18, but is not completed until age 21. Logically, we could expect that on completion and maturation of nature's latest, largest, and highest brain at age 21 we could possess capacities more dramatically different from and more powerful than anything previously experienced. But, in fact, nothing much happens at all. Alexander and Lange in Oxford University Press' "Higher Stages of Human Development: Adult Growth Beyond Formal Operations," showed as each developmental stage offers more advanced intelligence, a significantly smaller percentage of our population achieves that stage. When the secondary prefrontal neural form is ready for full functioning, nothing seems to happen that is in any way commensurate with the newness, size and long drawn out formation of the complete prefrontal cortex.

The primary prefrontal functions, formed in the earliest years, continues but there is little to indicate an evolutionary shift of function and behavior or revolutionary change in life, as can be rightfully expected. Could it be that the unexplained architectural remains in the Baalbek mountains of Lebanon, the architectural studies of Machu Picchu in Peru and the mound builders of North America in Ohio, Indiana, Illinois, and Poverty Point in Louisiana are examples of civilizations that did succeed in greater fulfillment of their prefrontal cortex. As further example, many gifted artists reach a summit of accomplishment, yet commit suicide or become victims of premature death.

Generativity allows us to let go of conscious, immediate reality, and experience the forces of the universe in totality. In the writer, especially the philosopher, one sees the constant striving to unify all knowledge. The total dynamic forces cannot be understood and can not be tolerated by a single human being. Sharing must occur to maintain a sense of balance and to prevent a loss of momentary reality. One might perceive duration or infinity and lose the ability to return to the moment in which one lives.

In truth, if one can move to generativity, one is essentially taking the first step into being a part of infinity, the feeling of growth. Read the works of Michener and observe from his nationality studies of *Hawaii* and *Iberia*, his growth through *The Source* to a beginning of human kind, and in *Centennial*[16] to the origins of the earth. At this point of evolutionary development, one can best appreciate the five analytic balances and the reason why I chose the term "balances."

The generative person, at the point of greatest involvement in his/ her work, will have a sense of all ten forces simultaneously operating. This simultaneity can only be accomplished in an individual who has a mature intimate relationship to provide strength when needed. If the generative person is lacking in sufficient intimacy and does not commit suicide, he/she will experience the inexorable movement toward isolation, then gradual personal diminution, loss of generativity, and finally to a state of apathy.

Most previously successful people cannot identify the specific causes of their fall from grace. They blame bad fortune, inattention, other people, or vague causes such as lack of confidence, choking up, or not maintaining a winning attitude. Apathy, resulting from a series of failures, personal losses and inability to rise above ones limits, can be a fatal condition.

Nevertheless, people in such moods have risen above their adversity with humor. A famous joke is worth relating in this context. A college football team with a long and illustrious tradition of winning finds itself the victim of a string of defeats. The school is prosperous and places no price limit on reversing the team's luck. It equips them with new uniforms, reduces their class requirements, brings in nutritionists and new coaches. Nothing changes their miserable performance. In desperation, they hire a retired army colonel famed for his ability to take mediocre recruits, athletic teams, and average companies and turn them into outstanding success stories. His experience indicates to him that most people and teams stop winning when they either no longer have competitive skills or lack a sense of commitment to their goal. He wastes no time telling this idea directly to the team. "What I want to know", he barks at them in the gymnasium, "Is whether you guys just don't understand the game you're supposed to be playing or if you're all just apathetic?" He scans their faces to see if his words have struck a nerve, but no one seems to change expression, except the team captain, Higgins. "Higgins? Which is it?" he prompts. "Aw, coach," he laments tiredly, "I don't know and I don't care!"

On Becoming a Generative Person

The steps become more difficult and more complex, and yet a quiet simplicity begins to invade the movement of life. As one begins to feel and understand the forces of the universe, one can become totally overwhelmed at its majesty, the length of time it has existed, the way it continues to evolve. Yet, one must try to put oneself into perspective with all of that majesty. One now becomes more aware of his/her human needs—an internal process of assessing one's being, abilities, talents, energy, motivations—that is to say, one's assets. Then one must assess one's limitations or areas best left to others. This is the process of becoming objective about oneself. Before one can grow generatively, that person must experience this process of being objective about the self.

We can appreciate Einstein's difficulty deciding to focus his energy within a particular realm, realizing universe's status and its possible destination during his lifetime. Each person occupies the briefest moment in time in a particular life, but each one is an integral part of creation. It becomes a humbling experience to see oneself in perspective to creation. We need to be our unique self and generate what we can within that realm and simultaneously realize that one can only be his/herself. *Humility* manifests itself as evidence that one has become objective about oneself.

Gradually becoming objective essentially began during the process of achieving the capacity for intimacy. As we share ourselves with others, we also begin to see and to know ourselves through the other's eyes, awareness, and knowledge.

We come to a humble objective sense and knowledge of oneself when we continue to grow within the realm of our true abilities. It becomes equally important that we develop the ability to be objective about the outside world and about other people. Furthermore, the first genuine step toward this end begins during moments of intimacy—when we can enjoy the first genuine glimpses of objective knowledge about another person. Only with objective knowledge can we begin to use our ability to reason and decide, both will allow us to grow in a generative manner and be productive with our life's energy.

Maturity is defined
by the 3 As
of one's limitations:

Awareness
Acceptance
Appreciation

Chapter 11
Integrity versus Despair

Synopsis:

The need for Integrity arises when a generative person harmonizes his/her total life experience with one's universe.

For this harmony to occur , the individual must have developed Loyalty emerging from Personal Growth.

One now becomes accountable for all of one's being that is the past, present, and future. In psychoanalytical terms, accountability means unifying one's unconscious and conscious being.

Despair is the contradiction of Integrity. It often develops as a result of enormous struggles, and might ultimately lead to some form of suicide.

The simple outgrowth of developing Integrity is initiating, declaring faith in oneself. This outgrowth then expands to a faith in the dignity of all human life. Emerging is a preoccupation with self or narcissism to a genuine interest in the welfare of others, as well as one's self.

✳

The generative person may or may not enjoy a considerable life span before showing tangible results. If the individual is truly generative, he will one day want to make his total life experience harmonize with his universe. This awareness, of course, involves a person's total physical, mental, affectual, and spiritual being becoming harmoniously part of the totality of one's living, dynamic, and constantly evolving universe.

To develop integrity, one must possess loyalty. It is no small feat to face the struggles necessary to attain this quality. First, a human being must face all his actions in life and be accountable for them. Furthermore, it requires an accounting of his thoughts, wishes, and desires, no matter how foreign he may have felt at the time one has chosen to experience them. In psychoanalytic terms, it means unifying one's unconscious with one's conscious being. Finally, a merging occurs into a unified identity of one's past, present, and future. This unification is not a one-time process that one must experience to account for and accept all that one has become up to the present. Actually, one is forever more involved in the ongoing struggle to maintain integrity and move and grow beyond it.

The Roman Catholic Church devised a compelling concept to provide hope and solace to those who found this struggle too great. Although the Church has placed human beings in an enormous position of conflict for centuries, it touches on something profoundly intrinsic to humanness. "Vincible Ignorance" pointed out certain things about oneself that could realistically be understood. From that moment of comprehension, one would be accountable. "Invincible Ignorance" provided a loophole to the unconscious being and, in effect, said areas of one's being could not be understood, and human beings were therefore free from accountability.

When a human being reaches the level of struggling for integrity, he/she can no longer accept that principle. One is accountable ultimately for all of one's being.[21] A totally harmonious universe depends on it.

I personally see the universe moving in that direction despite the many problems, including many periods of regression necessary and purposeful to highlight ongoing problems. The process of therapy, with which I have struggled for more than forty years, has helped me to appreciate the way there is always an increase in symptoms that look and feel like regression, as one more closely approaches the crucial and underlying conflicts. The analysis of resistances and defenses is the core of the therapy process. The dedicated therapist after a time with his/

her patient relishes the appearance of such symptoms, because he/she knows something vitally important is near.

Human beings must ultimately reach a position of no longer accepting concepts such as "not guilty by reason of insanity." All human beings are identical in essence, and that sameness ultimately means being responsible for oneself totally. One cannot hope to reach this position as long as one continues to advocate and promote feelings of guilt (the loss of worth of one's total being) and the process of punishment.

Yes, we have a long, long way to go. I see the recurring appearance of the issue of capital punishment highlighting the human struggle with the issue of pride in one's sexuality versus a guilt over one's sexuality. As pointed out in the Initiative versus Guilt chapter, one can only begin to move toward a responsibility as one begins to take pride in all that is inherent in oneself.

Because sexuality is the essential moving force behind all activity as the process of becoming one with one's universe, a person must abandon the realm of guilt and punishment in favor of pride, before he can begin to accept full responsibility for his total being.

In essence, human behavior can become understandable no matter how crazy, criminal, psychotic, or sociopathic it appears to be. It is true that some people may have to be constrained by society for protection, but the punitive judgmental concept must evolve.

This evolvement is already occurring despite the present wave of renewed interest in capital punishment, more strenuous prison terms, and the construction of more prisons. As the cost of punishment increases without a corresponding decrease in the cost of crime, society must evaluate the quality and functional usefulness of its criminal justice system.

The contradiction to Integrity is Despair. With the enormous struggles one endures facing oneself, it is understandable that some individuals with enormous life struggles may turn to despair. When a society arrives at a particular place in its history, it may have little room for an individual whose integrity, or struggle for it, requires one to be opposed to society. History is sadly often a rendition of this fact. Despair can be viewed, therefore, as an approach to integrity on an active, dynamic plane that needed to move to a more passive position. Despair's ultimate expression may be in the last act of suicide or moving to another pole of silence.

1. We need to consider the essential feeling of loyalty. How does one come to a feeling of loyalty? Here one begins to come full circle with him/herself. One's first loyalty remains focused on the self. Remember Hegel's quote: "There is nothing so unyielding as the singularity of my self-awareness." Specifically, one will realize the nature of loyalty is crucial to all the essential needs described within this work, as noted in the following: Trust through Unconditional Love

2. Autonomy through Aloneness

3. Initiative through Pride in one's sexuality

4. Expansiveness through Fun

5. Identity through Specificity

5. Intimacy through Openness

7. Generativity through Growth

8. Integrity through Loyalty

Throughout existence, these essential human needs will continue to exert themselves. Human beings are given the marvelous opportunity to rework each of the steps whenever they arise. I offer the insight of several wise individuals. Always stay in touch with young people. They will continue to let one know all that is new and evolving in the universe.

All of the previous points are vital, but if I were to emphasize one, it would be the need to be loyal to pride in one's sexuality. It is our energy source! Furthermore, it alone can be the source of the mature feeling of passion. For human beings to fulfill that deep inner feeling that they might continue forever (perhaps human beings do), it is necessary to develop a consistent capacity for passion and tenderness.

On Achieving Integrity

It is difficult to discuss integrity and the search for it because its truth is so direct, simple, and unavoidable. If one is able to experience these steps of objectivity—coming to know oneself and accept responsibility for one's total being for all time, maintain the position of loyalty to oneself and one's needs—then one has experienced a process of declaration of faith in oneself. To arrive at a position of faith, one must have felt very deeply each of the many processes described in this book. Gradually, from an internal feeling to an ultimate concern for understanding and knowing, through much study, internal reflection, patience and caring, a feeling of sweet sadness transpires as one sees his/her life come to fruition.

As Fromm described in *The Art of Loving*,[13] it is rational faith borne of one's own feelings and learning experiences, as opposed to irrational faith borne of acceptance of outside power or authority. Faith in oneself gives birth to integrity, and must expand to a faith in all humanness and human beings. This faith in the importance and dignity of all human life and faith in the potentiality for human growth ultimately progresses to a faith in the evolutionary growth of the universe. As a result of this initial emergence of faith, one can begin to see emergence from preoccupation with self or narcissism to a genuine interest in the welfare of others, as well as the self.

Passion is the
drive to
aggressively incorporate
the forces of the
universe with an intense
bridled form of that
aggressiveness—namely,
tenderness.

Chapter 12
Passion versus Tenderness

Synopsis:

Passion is the desire to aggressively encompass and incorporate the forces of the universe. It ultimately requires a sharing between two equally generative individuals of integrity and the need to incorporate the power of the universe.

As we come to the realization of the giving, nurturing nature of the universe, one learns that to give is to feel and become a part of life and the processes of the universe.

The subtle, yet powerful, contradiction to Passion is Tenderness that arises from restraint, understanding, compassion, and forgiveness—all of which require great personal strength. Tenderness is an acceptance of the ultimate truth of the universe, of which we are an essential vital link, but never as powerful as the entire universe.

A generative person with integrity begins to find a degree of balance understanding the entire forces of the universe with an intimate relationship that provides understanding and stability. A quest then arises to become fully one with those universal forces.

A desire arises to include the strength, intensity, energy, and eternity of the universe as part of oneself. Not to have that wholeness with the energy of one's universe would be analogous to separating oneself from one's creation, from the vitality of life itself. Passion is the drive to encompass and incorporate aggressively the forces of the universe. It assumes the quality of possessiveness. It is more than a binding or becoming a part of the universal energy; it is a desire to make all of that energy one's own. Furthermore, the need to share this desire via an intimate relationship is essential to maintain balance and bring understanding. Here passion begins to make itself known in the relationship between two people. I use passion to describe an intimate sharing (between two equally generative individuals of integrity) of the need to incorporate the power of the universe.

A need for each other exists to possess the strength of the universe. It is not a need to possess the other, but a need for each other to gain fulfillment of the self's need to possess the energy of the universe.

An even deeper awareness arises. Giving one's total energy to the universe through another individual allows us to become a part of the strength of the universe, because at this point one genuinely feels and knows the giving nature of the universe. Creation nurtures human beings whenever they become participants in its energy. To give is to feel and become a part of life and the process of the universe.

As in other natural systems, a subtle contradiction begins to evolve. If one did take possession of the universe's energy, one could face the risk of destroying or distorting the natural universe through one's aggression. Even more likely, the risk exists of establishing one's own destruction by attempting to possess something which is much more powerful than oneself. The contradictory force of tenderness is therefore a most powerful process that arises from this drive. Power derives more clearly from restraint, understanding, compassion, and forgiveness than it does from brute force or threat. It becomes a form of universal leverage. At the same time, only someone enormously strong can be gentle or tender. If not, gentle or tender, those actions would not, be the result of choice (free will). They would be the only behavior that a timid, weak, or powerless individual could exhibit.

Tenderness is an acceptance of the ultimate universal truth, of which human beings are an essential link. However, they are never individually as powerful as the entire universe. One becomes unified with the universe and therefore able to possess its energy. At the same moment, one is separate and unable to possess or use his/her total energy. (Recall the fourth of the five analytical balances.) No more beautiful example avails itself of the contradictory, yet complementary, processes in the nature of humanness than in the struggle between the forces of passion and tenderness.

These struggles have the universal quality of a supreme, beautiful truth whether depicted in art, literature, stage, film, or in the ultimate drama of day-to-day existence. Often the struggle of one being occurs to contain within him/herself elements seemingly too powerful and contradictory to be contained safely within the fragile limitations of the human person. Nonetheless, miraculously, human beings not only contain this maelstrom of power, but they transcend it and, with careful gradual steps, bequeath it to loved ones.

If one is perceptive, one can sense underneath that tenderness is an intense bridled form of aggressive desire. Uniquely, in true passion, one can also detect a sweet sense of tenderness. It is a remarkable experience to be involved with individuals who exhibit both of these qualities toward one's chosen field of endeavor. Even more, when two people with a relationship of intimacy, generativity, and integrity begin to add passion and tenderness, other people—and, yes, even the world—take notice.

At this point, an internal chemistry can occur between two evolved or intrinsically natural people, and then passion occurs. One can flow with passion, if it is present. People often talk about "adding passion" to their lives, but they usually mean excitement. Passion is more of a natural outpouring when people have established the proper emotional foundation. Certain creations of nature can hardly be improved. Natural passion is one of these perfect creations. One hopes eternally to experience passion because "A life without passion seems no life at all." (Schulte)

It is never enough for humans to find something pleasant or enjoyable. They yearn for the full enrichment of the senses, and become sick and dull if they do not discover things for which they can feel passion. Human beings search their entire lives to find the genuine calling, the true love, the true faith, anything that promises to distill pure undiluted passion without compromise, without fault, without restraint, and without harmful side effects or satiety.

Satiety is the fatal trap that awaits the passionate or passion-seeking human beings. Many artists, including musicians, painters, sculptors, and writers have often described experiences of boundless energy while creating a new work. Clearly, their unity with the energy of the universe becomes a driving force, often resulting in many hours to days of a continuous flow of energy that becomes difficult to stop. Even after completing the work, most of the geniuses have intimate soul mates who help them to maintain balance; or otherwise, they struggle with depression or suicide.

One of the beautiful examples to behold is a couple who have mutually discovered and developed their passion. Dance partners and ice skating pairs exhibit a soaring symphony of energy in their artistic productions. The exhilarating bursts of powerful dynamic energy are classically counterpointed by interludes of subtle movements of tenderness.

We must now bring up the most basic contradictory feeling to passion and tenderness: indifference. To treat one's life energy with indifference becomes a dangerous and powerful phenomenon. If one becomes indifferent toward oneself or any part of one's life, such as one's work or one's universe, the person is then capable of manipulating all things to any end. Sayings abound for this kind of manipulation, namely, "The end justifies the means"; "Life is only for the moment";

"If it feels good, then do it." One's desire to be one with oneself and one's universe is lost and converted to an unending quest for power through manipulation because feeling has ceased to exist. If one ceases to feel, he/she is a robot in search of power, capable of any monstrous or destructive act. One need look no further than the biblical quotation, "So then because thou art lukewarm, and neither cold nor hot, I will spue thee out of my mouth." (Revelation 3:16)

This act is an enormous growth step. Many who approach it may rationalize that they have done enough in life and find it time to retire. On the other hand—on an optimistic note—as longevity and good health are extended, many people do not retire. They remain active and discover the true nature of unselfish giving through volunteerism.

"Only through union in
the process of loving
can true knowing be
possible."

Eric Fromm

"First you feel,
then you
know."

Jerome L. Schulte

Chapter 13
Love versus Power

Synopsis:

Love is an intimate union—physically, mentally and spiritually—of two mature adult human beings. Love requires the feeling of promise or commitment borne by faith in oneself of both individuals. A mutual faith in the relationship follows. Nietszche defined "the ability to promise" as the distinguishing quality of Humanness.

"*The Art of Loving*" by Eric From and a quotation from "The Philosophy of Law" by Hegel add depth to an understanding of Love.

The contradiction to Love is to control through the use of Power, which destroys the vital forces of contradiction, thus destroying Humanness and the need to grow via feelings.

✳

I have refrained from using the word love because the discussion of unconditional Love is the prerequisite for the development of trust in the first year of life. We are finally ready to approach that much maligned, poorly understood, yet most needed and desired feeling in life.

The most vital work I have encountered on the subject of love is Eric Fromm's "*The Art of Loving.*"[13] Fromm, in his genius, underemphasized the enormity of the difficult work in the emotional growth that must be accomplished before anyone can begin to enter the arena described by the author in his book. This realization, plus my own need to be loved and my desire to love, inspired me to write this book.

My favorite quotation from Hegel's *Philosophy of Law* follows.[22]

The work has provided rich material for reflection for more than forty years. I still uncover thought-provoking mysteries entwined within it like cleverly buried treasure.

> "The first moment in love is the fact that I do not want to be for myself an independent person, and that I, were this the case, would feel defective and incomplete. The second moment is that I win my independence in another person, that I am affirmed in that person, and vice versa. Thus love is the most formidable contradiction, which the mind cannot resolve. For there exists nothing as unyielding as the singularity of my self-awareness which must be negated, and which yet I need to have affirmed. Love is both the creation and resolution of this contradiction, as its resolution it is moral communion."

Because of the "vital force" that results from the contradictions in mature love, Fromm was able to state one requirement as proof that genuine mature love exists. Each person will become more of an individual than he/she was prior to the establishment of mature love. (Recall the principle "that a relationship must experience the same growth steps as an individual" is also valid in terms of a relationship following generativity and integrity before love can occur.)

I do not equate intimacy with mature, adult, human love. Intimacy is a prerequisite to establish a love relationship, but intimacy can exist without mature love being necessarily present. Intimacy does not require or depend on sexuality or any physical expression or act. It can be simply a state of casual, comfortable familiarity, which siblings, soldiers, lodge or tribal members share.

Love, as I choose to define it, is "An intimate union, physically, mentally, and spiritually of two adult human beings." I include the word spiritually because, in my definition of sexuality, the concept of becoming one with oneself and one's universe implies becoming one with the creator of one's universe. Such a creator is as inseparable from his creation as the artist is inseparable from his work.

I would like to share Sandor Rado's following three criteria as evidence of the existence of mature adult love:[23]

1. Both individuals successfully achieve physical and emotional orgasm on a quite regular basis with each other.
2. The relationship is able to sustain periods of considerable separation.
3. A degree of altruism allows the happy establishment and fulfillment of a family.

Hidden in these three criteria is the blueprint of a mature love relationship, namely, the feeling of promise or commitment. This feeling is borne from the development of faith in oneself by both people and from the evolvement of faith in the relationship between the two. Nietszche long ago defined the ability to promise as the distinguishing quality of humanness.[24] The lack of faith in oneself and the inability to have faith in others or the quality of humanness leads to the development of the contradiction to love, which is the attempt to control through the use of power. Power is the destruction of the vital forces of contradiction in life. Therefore, it destroys humanness by destroying the need to grow through feeling.

As individual human beings and as partners in relationships with others, human beings have a long road ahead of them. The struggles we will experience pursuing issues with Iran, Russia, China, The United Nations Nuclear Regulatory Commission, and The UN Human Rights Committee (reorganized in 2006 as a result of ongoing failures of the previous committee) are enormous. One hopes this will eventually evolve to a more loving relationship between the United States and these important countries and organizations.

As Fromm pointed out, only through union in the process of loving can true knowing be possible. To love is to know. "First you feel, then you know." (Schulte) Fromm superbly outlined the factors necessary for the practice and the development of the art of loving, namely, discipline, concentration, patience, and supreme concern.[13] He clearly pointed out that "I love from the essence of my being—and experience the other person in the essence of his or her being." In essence, all human beings are identical. On this premise, I have based this entire work. From this essential point, I have also constructed my position that "Once one has loved, one can love again." Each human being will vary regarding his/her ability for multiple, simultaneous love relationships.

The need for
ever-continuing growth
through feelings
is the essence of our
humanness.

Chapter 14
Conception versus Stagnation

Synopsis:

Altruism verifies a genuine love relationship and distinguishes the capacity of human beings to complete another link in the evolutionary process of the universe. Simultaneously, each individual is able to complete another growth step and fulfill his/her destiny with another mature living being.

Stagnation is the contradiction of Conception and delays the process of one's growth through some form of manipulation, trying to use power to avoid the need for struggle and growth. This chapter and Section I close with an exposé of some struggles faced by our current society.

*

Now, it is time to examine more closely the third point for determining the presence of a mature adult love relationship. The way in which altruism begins to evolve, whereby two people are able to give of themselves without needing always to receive equal return. Ideally at this point, two people are ready and able emotionally to begin a genuine process of conception. It is now possible for two people (acting individually and in unison) to create another human being. In this way the ideal physical beginning of another human life is purposely initiated. This process provides a method for two people to complete another link in the evolutionary process of the universe, and one that simultaneously fulfills another step of growth for each individual. All higher forms of animal life have the ability to breed/mate, to reproduce, but human beings acting from the mutual basis of love are the only earthly creatures unique in their ability to plan and seek actively the responsibility of parenthood.

We are all an intimate part of the universe and enjoy an individual identity and a role in the total evolutionary process. To fulfill our role in the evolutionary process of the universe requires that we strive to fulfill our individual and group potential to its maximum. "First you become a person, then you become a couple, then the path is ready for extending oneself into the total process of the universe through conception." (Schulte)

Consider for a moment the parent or parent(s) positioned to desire and attain the manipulative tool of power. Because the child will be a "thing," a "possession," and not a conception designed to fulfill the individual's personal or universal identity, they can not give unconditional love to the child. Indeed, the act of conception was manipulative, selfish, and conditional or, worse, simply accidental and undesired.

The dilemma of abortion arises as promised in Chapter Two. The real issue is not the moment that a human existence begins to have value. That idea is ridiculous because everything that is a part of creation and the universe has value. The proposition arises that matter can essentially neither be created nor destroyed, merely rearranged. The decision, therefore, about conception must move in the direction of individual choices. It always has and always will proceed in that manner.

Similarly, the physical lives of people will be terminated by others in many ways as has always been the case—and perhaps many as yet undreamt of methods in the future. It would be a tenuous argument to suggest humans, at different stages of their lives, have intrinsically different innate values or the right to life. Either human beings all have this innate value and right to life or they do not. This value means that all people of all ages of every conceivable race, color, creed, or no creed, brilliant, slow-witted, handicapped, morally upright, depraved, law-abiding, or criminal all have the same intrinsic right. If only God can create life, then according to this argument, only God can destroy it.

This agreement is not necessarily the actual reality of the situation, but if one chooses to argue from a religious conviction for the rights of the unborn, then this reasoning must be applied to the entire human condition, not conveniently at the moment of conception.

Each and every individual human being will determine his/her own course regarding these so-called moral issues, such as abortion and murder. Society may need to create legal issues to maintain balance, but those issues change as society changes. The beauty and mystery of creation is that human beings have the inherent freedom to choose their own direction.

I am proposing that souls, like all matter, are created by the creator. Souls will find matter or a human life of which to become a part. Inherently, I feel there is some vision of the possibilities to a soul before it chooses to enter into a physical life that has been conceived. Some of those possibilities include the risk of abortion, the risk of some genetic or physical handicap, the risk of an abusive parent, or the risk of early disease, disability and accidental death. In other words, some level of choice is involved.

The issue also arises, and has been long debated, regarding the need to be reborn (i.e. Julia Roberts' recent profession of becoming a Hindu)—however many times it is necessary in order to determine one's personal, universal, and spiritual identity. Certainly, many individuals have a sense of "having been here before" and a powerful sense of needing to "complete various tasks this time around." I was particularly influenced when I attended my six children's births, that in this early infancy, some had the feeling and aura of "older souls" while others had the sense of being "newer souls." One does see recurrent themes presenting themselves in people's lives for further work until these issues are mastered and people proceed to new challenges.

Currently, the USA and its legislature (the state, federal and Supreme Courts), struggle with the intricacies of Roe versus Wade, late third trimester childbirth issues, definitions of sexuality in marriage and civil unions, and most recently and powerfully the issue of stem cell research. The opening of this new frontier highlights the dynamic new arenas of knowledge that provide the intensity of feelings needed for dynamic growth. No choice is available regarding our essence! The need for ever-continuing growth through feelings is the essence of our humanness.

The way a human being will pursue that internal dynamic of need to grow is one's freedom to choose. It is amazingly beautiful that our world society is now dealing with issues of conception. Whether our world society can use this issue as a necessary stepping stone as outlined in this book for its continued growth remains to be seen.

When individuals decide to conceive a child, they choose to conceive or to delay the process of one's growth through some form of manipulation. This idea leads to my premise that if one manipulates in life rather than struggles with growth, one is essentially stagnating one's growth in the evolutionary process of the universe.

Manipulation is therefore defined as a decision to delay or stagnate one's own and the universe's evolutionary growth. It is important to realize a person exists in an internal dynamic process in the middle of this stagnation. Each individual also plays a vital role in the physical and spiritual evolution of the universe.

Former President Nixon is a famous, or infamous, example of someone who proceeded in the direction of power and manipulation with eventual stagnation.[26, 26] He struggled with his internal dynamic need to regain a degree of positive impetus to grow. Eventually, he was able to remove himself from an indifference to others and overcome his quest for power. He came to an equilibrium, even an odd sort of redemption within society as he gained a greater sense of value for his family, friends, and common citizens.

The former President is widely remembered for his misdeeds, but he is held in far greater esteem now than ten years ago. Did the public simply forget? No, the late former President used his retired life to diligently develop methods of improving relations between nations, his family, and the American public without bitterness, complaint, or rancor.[24] Ultimately, he achieved a form of decency and respect from his failures and disgrace—one he never achieved when he had the most powerful job on earth.

Within this contradiction is a sublime and powerful lesson for all current or would-be persons of power or influence. Just as all human beings contain "the seeds of their own destruction," that is a fatal flaw or character weakness, so does each one contain a universe of resources, hidden talents, sterling qualities, and strength of character often undiscovered until elicited by a crisis, failure, or traumatic incident. For this reason the symbol in Chinese for the word crisis can also be read as opportunity.

A crisis of one kind or another seems to elicit the best or the worst traits in people, and strangely the person who emerges "flawed" from one crisis can suddenly emerge phoenix-like as a "hero" from another crisis. For this reason alone, one should never judge people by only one trait or event. Human beings are always tripping and falling in one race, but moving forward to win other races by many lengths. One must appreciate the vast potential of people to change, improve, and remake their lives if given a chance.

It would be simultaneously naive and foolish to expect individuals who are habitually violent or dangerous to alter their behavior easily, simply because they were given more chances. Some individuals cannot demonstrate the genuine human qualities of compassion or caring, but have only learned to mimic these feelings to manipulate others selfishly.

Identifying the potentially dangerous individuals from those who have simply had a momentary character failure is a serious and important task that confronts the US social and legal system. Furthermore, can some violent or disturbed individuals be reformed or altered by therapy, religious conversion, drug regimens, or genetic manipulation? Yes, the evidence suggests this idea is becoming more possible.

The future promises to become fertile with the means of rebuilding improperly made human beings, if they are bold and progressive in their attempts to apply these new methods. A grim future alternative could also make these methods the tools of a power-hungry minority bent on breaking and controlling the masses. Such a potential and frightening abuse of power must be fought diligently by people of good will who value human dignity and a free society.

The Schulte Immortality Complex that drives humans toward greater cosmic integration, freedom, tolerance, and universal union can be subverted into the dark manipulative struggle for power, repression, and control. Human beings are always warned about the dangers of anarchy, lawlessness, and chaos, but they are not warned often enough about the dangers of too much centralized power, too many repressive laws, and stringent conformity that will break the spirit as well as stifle imagination and creativity. I hope this book will in some small way provide a modest blueprint for developing the positive means of establishing a solid foundation of humanness to prevent such a dark scenario.

SECTION II

The Physical Universe:
A Study of the Criminal Personality

All human beings
have two sides
to their personalities
with contradictory
forces that wage war.

Chapter 1
The Other Side of the Coin

Synopsis:

One assumes the position that to gain understanding of the criminal personality, society must relinquish its judgmental, moralistic attitude. Prototypes of this process are organizations and programs for alcoholics and homosexuals. These groups not long ago were considered criminal, then deemed ill. Now they are seen as people exerting freedom of choice with responsibilities attached to those choices. Such traits or groups and other criminal attitudes have been considered the dark side of humanity, much like the New World was once the dark side of the planet before being explored. Similarly, we usually consider the tail side of the coin somehow ominous and less valued than the head side. Both sides contribute equally to the intrinsic value of a coin. One can understand both sides of the human personality contribute equally to the intrinsic value of humanness.

It is essential to remember all human beings have value. Therefore, we should recognize the need for all humans to grow through a continual development of their feelings. It continues throughout life and through each and every existence of human soul.

In the recent past, the mentally ill were considered to be possessed by demons or devils. Society has often explained the criminal personality as the work of the devil as well. Such was the attitude of Catholicism toward homosexuals at the end of the 20th century, until it became fairly common knowledge that many of its own priests were participating in this "devilish" behavior.

The mental health movement has made it possible for society to see all individuals have some neurotic "hang-ups." An individual should not be discriminated against or persecuted at will. The so-called alcoholics have also emerged to demand acceptance as ordinary humans beings with ordinary problems. The gay-lesbian movement has enjoyed the greatest success of any group taking their label out the diagnostic nomenclature. While recently testifying in a case of dissociative reaction, I was startled to agree with a district attorney that it is foreseeable that the entire psychiatric diagnostic manual may some day be discarded. This work presupposes just such a "radical" concept.

Certainly, the APA's *Diagnostic S Manual IV* requires us to be far more specific applying labels to individuals, although it simultaneously makes more categories available to the diagnostician. I am emphasizing that all people dwell on the same continuum. The criminal personality is going to have to be recognized as one of the many possibilities that human beings adopt in their lives. We will eventually be forced to abandon the moral attitude that certain people are bad and others are good.

The alcoholic, like the homosexual, was long considered a criminal; however, he is now considered ill and one day will be similarly seen as exerting freedom of choice and accepting the responsibility attached to it. The same essential process will eventually occur for the criminal personality. In short, criminals are people with dysfunctional or altered physiological or mental processes, not evil or "possessed by the devil."

For now, the possible comparison to a coin with two sides may be the most easily understood metaphor. Consider all individuals are on one or the other side of the coin, which represents the universe of people. Until recently, the African- or Mexican-American people in the

United States were considered by many Caucasians as being the tail side of the coin, while considering themselves the head side. This example is used because African- and Mexican-Americans comprise the majority in the US prison system. Autism, schizophrenia, affective psychoses, and criminal personalities can presently be likened to the other side of the coin, the tail side (the dark side) much like Africa was once considered the dark continent because it was unexplored and poorly understood. Although, the tail side of a coin is not given high regard, and disdained by many, it contributes value to a coin equal to the head side.

All human beings have two sides to their personalities. We all have struggles between the contradictory forces that wage war within us. As Section I illustrated, the dark side of our personality is as intrinsic as the bright side and sets up what we will begin to discover are necessary and vital contradictions. You will likely be amazed by the new awareness of our humanness that will emerge as we arrive at a complete understanding of this other side of our coin.

Section II, explores the other side of the coin that prevails in all of us, although more apparent in some than in others.

After conception, each soul
or human being
is already involved
in a dynamic process of
evolution.

Chapter 2
The Criminal Personality as a
Stage in the Process of Human Evolution

Synopsis:

The basic premise from Conception versus Stagnation, Section I, states "As the soul enters life through conception, it already occupies some level of its evolutionary development." The criminal personality rejects human contact, touch, or cuddling with frequent extremes of isolation and withdrawal, including a sensitivity to inanimate objects and remarkable feats of memory. It can be compared to variable states of autism. The crucial experience in the evolutionary development of the criminal personality is an altered experience through touch with a loving human being.

✳

It is time to consider the need for souls to evolve via feelings of growth to their highest possible state of completion. As defined in Section I, most people die prematurely of some form of self-destruction and at some level of incomplete evolution. A basic premise in my last chapter on Conception versus Stagnation suggests souls within the universe occupy different stages of evolutionary growth (matter can neither be created nor destroyed). As the soul enters life through conception, it already occupies some level of its evolutionary development, unless it is an entirely new and originally created soul, which asks the central question whether 'The Creator" is still actively creating. This subject of active creation cannot be fully explored until after this section discussing the essence of the physical universe. The central thesis of the present work is the study of the criminal personality. The spiritual universe is the subject of discussion in Section III.

That each soul or human being, following conception, is already involved in a dynamic process of evolution is vital to better understand the criminal personality. We must understand the stage at which they are involved in the dynamic process of evolution. Only then can we effectively understand criminal behavior and initiate a rational approach to help their personal evolutionary process. In turn, this undertaking should also promote the evolutionary growth of the universe, as it applies to the aggregate of intelligent consciousness.

Let us consider those children having early infantile autism that seems to inhibit affective relationships with people in their environment. This inability is characterized by extreme isolation, withdrawal, and outright rejection of human contact, touch, or cuddling. In contradiction, there seems to be a sensitivity to inanimate objects and remarkable feats of memory, which strangely and coincidentally is also true of the criminal personality.

It would be constructive to consider the criminal personality from the basic viewpoint that he/she has an altered ability concerning unconditional love and basic trust through the vital medium of touch. The altered ability might be the result of severe neglect in touching and unconditional loving early in life or through severe physical abuse, which is an extreme example of touch. Many children at birth, frequently in the most severe cases of early infantile autism, are found incapable of accepting unconditional love, even when fully available and freely offered.

I propose that multiple and variable states are observed in achieving trust and feelings of worth through unconditional love, and that the crucial experience in the criminal personality is an altered experience in touch with a loving human being. To understand these people, one must understand their experiences with the sense of touch. Only then does one have a genuine basis for designing programs which can effect a major beneficial revolution in society.

I consider the criminal personality a significant stage in the process of human evolution, occurring in an essentially different realm of the universe. Do not be surprised to discover a new form of logic is involved, and a willingness to understand this new form of logic, including an altered set of ethics, values, and morals. I am not suggesting the abolition of ethics, values, and morals, but simply adopting a new set of benchmarks as a basis for a truly realistic and firm foundation for establishing guidelines that actually reflect the working mechanisms of human thought and behavior.

This adoption requires a brash boldness and unswerving dedication to accept the truth of the matter regarding human behavior—no matter how unsettling or contradictory the results may appear at first glance. Humans are comfortable with their illusions and myths, and they are most violent in defense of their cherished illusions, particularly those that could cast doubt on the most personal and most hidden weaknesses or flaws. Be cautious, but open-minded, keeping uppermost in mind the fearful truth with which the hunter can easily become the hunted, and the "law-abiding citizen," suddenly becomes the criminal, depending on the social convulsions society may be experiencing.

Touch, especially
the need for human touch,
essentially defines a
person's need
for boundaries in the
reality of one's life span
in the affectual
universe.

Chapter 3
Autism

Synopsis:

Human touch, especially the need for human touch, essentially defines the need for boundaries in the affectual universe. Criminal personalities are souls at an evolutionary point where they no longer need human affectual relationships, as much as they need an expanded sense of being one with the physical universe. With the priority of achieving a universal identity, rather than a socially acceptable one, comes a value system not based on consideration of other people's feelings and values. The difficulties remaining adjusted to society while moving from a personal to a universal identity are highlighted in a discussion of variable degrees of autism.

This chapter considers the severely autistic child who is incapable of establishing an effective relationship with people and rejects human touch. Often he has keen sensitivity, trusts nonhuman things, and distrusts apparently loving human beings.

If we reflect for a moment, we are reminded that each human has at least one thing which is all-important to him/her. It is usually an inanimate object which a person holds dear. Each person, therefore, identifies or "feels one" with an inanimate object, aware of being one with the self in relationship with the inanimate universe. In this sense, our personal universe consists of our self-awareness, as well as our attachment to special objects or objects of devotion.

Touch—especially the need for human touch—essentially defines our need for boundaries in our life span in the affectual universe. Human touch, therefore, reflects the depth of personal existence in the immediate reality.

The inability to be touched by another human being during moments of deep inner need can frequently have shattering consequences on the person's psyche. If we pursue such a fear of shattering to the ultimate, we become aware of the eventual personal dissolution into the background of the universe.

This dissolution can be compared, metaphorically, to a meteor dissolving portion by portion as it enters the atmosphere and burns up. It is also reminiscent of the Buddhist concept of individual reintegration into the universe, when one has achieved the ultimate state of Nirvana. In the Eastern mind, such a merging with the universal, including a sort of blessed state of mindless bliss, has been held as something very desirable. To the Western thinker—and I stress the word thinker—such an annihilation is usually extremely threatening.

I propose that the newborn who rejects human touch and unconditional love is merely at a different position in the evolutionary process. At this point, it is too early to make a judgment whether the autistic child might be less or more highly evolved than the child who adjusts to human touch. Certainly there is ongoing struggle within the autistic child regarding touch, and this struggle needs to be more thoroughly understood. We should be mindful of the way individuals reside in a state of flux with their evolving environment, of which they are a part as well as a participant.

The individual soul in everyone resides in a particular state of development in our universal evolution. This view I personally hold, although it is unnecessary to understand personality development within society. Even so, I believe those who wish to appreciate this subject matter fully will arrive at a similar viewpoint in their own time, through their own experiences.

My work most basically deals with the internal, dynamic, evolutionary, and developmental processes in each of us. The important point at this juncture centers on realizing that the internal dynamic processes in each human being and the process of the physical universe's evolutionary development are infinite dynamic processes. They are constantly evolving and changing.

Consider the child who is conceived as part of a manipulation from the mother's or father's viewpoint (for simplification, consider merely the mother's viewpoint). He can absorb those feelings or vibrations of manipulation while in the uterus and part of the mother for nine months. Many vital questions arise.

From the child's viewpoint, the world he enters is certainly not one of unconditional love or intrinsic value. Since inception, the embryo has been literally touched with manipulation and enters life after already experiencing nine months of never being certain of the true intent (except that it is manipulative) of the mother. Therefore the embryo can be considered preconditioned to distrust human touch. He will have to rely on his own internal sensations, than on the messages given through touch from the mother.

We should also remember this soul was a part of the larger physical universe, which it experiences in its environment once outside of the uterus. Then, one possibility exists for it being more secure and sensitive to the external inanimate world. Such a viewpoint presumes individual souls have uniquely different capabilities or differing natures, clearly as complex and different as the genetic blueprint the body imposes on the persona of the individual.

Another major dynamic force should be considered to understand the child who has difficulty with affectual or feeling relationships with other human beings. This other possibility concerns the autistic child who may have been conceived in a mother who indeed loves the child unconditionally during her pregnancy and after birth. This concept is much more difficult to grasp. To better understand of these dynamics, we must first assume a nonmoralistic and nonjudgmental position about the individuals involved. We may find ourselves continually posing the following questions: What are the dynamic forces? What is the process that has brought this individual to this particular point at this particular time? We can then remain inquisitive rather than fall into the error of becoming judgmental.

These children conceived in love and born into unconditional love—but who are nevertheless autistic—represent souls at an evolutionary point at which they may no longer need human affectual relationships as much as they need an expanded sense of being one with the physical universe. With this priority of achieving a universal identity rather than a personal, worldly, or socially acceptable identity comes a value system that does not consider other people's feelings to the great degree one casually expects. Indeed, one might have an insight into one of the striking qualities of the autistic child (which interestingly is also present in the so-called psychopath or social sociopath), namely, the apparent inability to learn from experience.

This quality is perhaps evidence of the integrity to maintain a universal identity viewpoint despite opposing the principles of one's customary earth bound, social, reality-based sense of conscience. No sense or feeling of guilt could exist when one feels conviction and integrity in the process of becoming one with one's universe. The reason is quite understandable (with the advent of diminishing guilt in our society) that mental health professionals are seeing more "character disorders" or "borderline people" as they are now called. The truth may well be that these human beings are truly "borderline" in the sense of becoming closer to being one with themselves and their universe, including their beginning to grasp the essence of the universe; whereas, previously they were only concerned primarily with personal identity and social acceptance.

The primitive personality attempts to uses guilt as a manipulative device. The psychopath does not believe in guilt, but is open, direct, and blunt about his/her actions. That is a different kind of integrity that society is compelled to invoke with a moral judgment of "bad" because the psychopath seeks a goal that offends society's own desires.

One may even understand the strength and unusual integrity within an organization like the Mafia. Little or no guilt exists in the face of every conceivable kind of physical carnage. Little manipulation is accomplished by the Dons. They control through direct power.

One may also reflect on the study of personalities such as Howard Hughes.[28] We marvel at the mixture of power out of touch with reality in a man like Mr. Hughes. He may be a prime example of an autistic person who had great personal and worldly power, but essentially lost his way in terms of being able to exist in the reality of ongoing society. We often see the corollary to this person in the "hardened repeat offender" who strangely has a sense of power and integrity but cannot exist in "normal" society. The Mafia chiefs are essentially another point on this continuum. They had great power and created their own society within which they must remain as restricted as the "repeat offender" who is restricted to his own society in prison.

It is important to realize the process of moving from a personal identity (that is quite attuned to adjust to a "normal" society) to a universal identity is, at present, most difficult to accomplish while remaining adjusted to society at large.

The question arises: Is it possible the autistic infant or child, who early in life is moving to an antisocial adjustment in society, is actually in search of a universal identity?

If so, how does one assist that process while simultaneously defining the steps of maintaining an integration with "normal" society? This process clearly seems to be a necessary part of a universal identity.

Most interesting and striking is that children identified as autistic early in life are often untracked as they enter into later school years and involvement with inanimate objects. If they are successful with these things, society does not demand they be affectual. Only those who somewhere along the road of life become aggressive within certain political or social power structures are labeled criminal personalities.

Senators, Presidents, and the CIA are often given the unlimited power to murder people deemed dangerous to them or society. Their crimes are permissible in such a society, just as the Mafia chiefs can murder certain people in their society and criminals in prison can murder certain people in their society.

The real issue involves struggling with the aggressive drives so they can become positive in an evolutionary way, rather than destructive to that which society in general considers to be its own best interests. Most "modern" societies abhor violence, yet train a warrior class to defend the self-interests of society, going to extreme lengths to retrain individuals so they can break the murder taboo in the name of national security, law enforcement, peace keeping, or other euphemisms.

The concepts of good or bad and guilt must first be abandoned, although it would be naive to think this abandonment could ever be anything but gradual. We can observe different levels of autism and, although the process in autism is identical, some individuals will become powerful people in the world without undue destructiveness. I believe the deciding factor depends on the degree of unconditional love already experienced by certain autistic souls during prior life spans, versus the lack of it leading to the destructive, autistic criminal personality. By the fruits of their labor or by their compatibility with things, we can know the difference. Those who enter life with prior unconditional love and integrity will stand a greater likelihood of becoming compatible and harmonizing with their universe. Those personalities without prior unconditional love in this life span will evince greater destructiveness.

Withdrawal from human touch and the aggressive reaction to it will tell the tale. Anyone with extended experience with juvenile delinquents is aware of the varying degrees of reaction to putting one's hand on their shoulders. I have found it to be valuable to predict amenability to traditional forms of therapy. Young adults or children who react excessively to a casual or gentle touch upon the shoulder are most often victims of physical, sexual, or psychological abuse. But in the context of the autistic child, such adverse reactions do not necessarily indicate this victimization at all.

Strangely, autistic children who are quite unresponsive to the touch of other human beings, respond remarkably well to the touch and affection of animals. Dogs, horses, dolphins, and porpoises have all proven amazingly more competent in therapeutic encounters with the extremely autistic than have traditional mental health care providers. It was also profound to see the change in autistic children enrolled in a surfing program on the East Coast. The news video showed how animated, smiling, and conversational the children became while on the surfboard compared to the exact opposite demeanor when off the boards. Is there something common regarding the way autistic children and animals regard their environment? Is there a heightened sensitivity to the needs of autistic children instinctively provided by creatures who routinely must use their sensory faculties to the fullest to survive and who can readily determine the actual sincerity or trustworthiness of a person or animal in mere moments?

All of these aspects are worthy of more detailed study, and will certainly reveal important clues to one's own deepest human and animal natures. I suspect the simple, more unconditional affection and love exhibited by these creatures is responsible to a great degree for the positive results that have been widely documented. Perhaps all that human beings need to accomplish is merely learning to emulate the same caring, unconditional, nonrigid, nonthreatening affection that the supposedly less-evolved fellow planetary inhabitants have known all along. We eagerly await new biomedical research that will develop out of the recent merger of autism groups and development of CAN (Cure Autism Now).

A sudy released by CDC (Center for Disease Control), March 29, 2012 announced the prevalence of autism spectrum disorders (ASD's) have surged in most recent years figures. It found that 1 in 88 8-year olds was classified in 2009 as having ASD versus 1 in 110 in 2006 and 1 in 153 in 2002. Prevalence increased across all sex, racial, ethnic, and cognitive functioning subgroups though much higher in boys compared with girls. No cause for ASD's is known. No single factor explains the changes in prevalence over the time period studied although it is speculated that greater awareness and earlier efforts at screening are substantially involved.

It is this author's opinion that this may be another elaboration of the process of biological transcendence. Studies are needed to determine possible correlation of these autism rates to the dynamic ongoing increase in brain size and neuronal connections survival rate at birth contrasted to their number at conception and first trimester. Just as we see an ever increasing presence of character disorder diagnosis and evolution of our society, I believe autism rate increase reflects an evolutionary phase of the universal personality that is increasingly becoming attuned to the physical universe.

Whereas the major manifestations of autism studied to date are of the inhibitory effects on personal active development there is an opposite side of the coin anti-inhibitory arena that has dramatically emerged simultaneously. The Borderline Personality, characterized by unstable relationships and distortion of one's self-image in dramatic ways, has had a rapidly increasing incidence now affecting one in fifty or two percent of the population compared to one in one hundred or one percent for autism. Brandon Marshall, the dominant wide receiver of the NFL Miami Dolphins, recent announcement of his borderline diagnosis and need for treatment classically illustrated his repeatedly dangerous unstable relationship with his wife and others along with his self-centered athletic explosiveness.

Feelings of the
criminal personality
are merely
"other-side-of-the-coin feelings"
contrasted to
"normal" affectual feelings,
which criminals repress with
aggressive acting-out behavior.

Chapter 4
The Aggressive Drive

Synopsis:

Aggression is the force or energy in a state or condition of unresolved process. Criminal personalities are human beings with the intrinsic need to grow through feelings to become one with themselves and their physical universes. Different processes help us become one with an inanimate physical universe, as opposed to an animate human affectual universe. The essence of the physical universe is energy and, the essence of the criminal personality is its aggressive energy to unify itself with the physical universe whose essence is energy.

Those who have been unable to have an affectual relationship as human beings, still have the ability for affectual relationships. It simply means their feelings are the contradictory feelings that a moralistic society imposes on them.

The feelings of the criminal personality are merely the other-side-of-the-coin feelings. The criminal personality, trying to focus on the physical universe, will need to eliminate "normal" feelings of the human affectual universe that would deny his/her chance of power. The criminal personality discovers aggressively acting out can repress normal human affectual feelings, to a great degree.

Although professionals tend to view such behavior from the perspective of aberrant or criminal behavior, this same behavior is exhibited by many people who strive for power or authority within society. However, they have found a niche in which such "antisocial" toughness seems acceptable or justified; namely, the police chief, the corporate CEO or manager, the bureaucrat, the super salesman, among others. One can thereby see the way compulsive thieves, exhibitionists, and rapists find their repeated acts diminish anxieties from the pressures of "normal" feelings and give them a feeling of power.

Work can be defined as an unconscious attempt to become one with the physical universe. It works well for the neurotic who thrives on unconscious processes, but is easily recognized by the criminal personality and the nonneurotic psychotic. Work, therefore, is not usually acceptable to these people. The criminal personality feels the universe should be there for the taking and aggressively attempts to do so. Every society in history has had its criminals, its crazies, and its normal people. Something basic, intrinsic, and vital exists in these personalities. Further study of the schizophrenic and psychotic personality will be undertaken in Section III.

Certainly it is time to understand the problem that has been with society throughout history. Understanding requires openness and a searching mind that is nonjudgmental. Society needs and is entitled to its own preservation, but should individuals and society blindly adhere to willful ignorance forever? Are the facts actually so threatening, the cure so much worse than the disease? Are human beings all too willing to be sick patients to one degree or another in an extremely disturbed, sick society that can only deteriorate further in its unbalanced condition the longer it tolerates and openly encourages this deceptive and cruel delusion of "normal" society? At what point does the condition of the macropatient (society) become so grave that members of society secede and form their own microcultures or countercultures as a tribal form of self-adjustment and spiritual healing?

Such profound rectification not only has occurred, but will occur more frequently and perhaps more radically in contrast to a "normal" society as stresses build. Without a reasonable methodology for correcting these distortions, violence and disaffection will become widespread, even epidemic by the beginning of the 22nd century. As the Chinese pictogram for change is interpreted, it either represents grave danger or immense opportunity. The way human beings deal with these issues will determine the nature of a future society.

Growth is the
essence of human energy
and energy of the
physical universe.
Both emanate from
inherent contradictions.

Chapter 5
On Energy

Synopsis:

The energy of the human affectual universe' and the physical universe' is infinite. A homogeneity in the laws of the affectual universe and the physical universe is contained in the mutual need for growth. Therefore, growth is the requirement of energy. Because the basis of energy lies in contradiction and arises from sexuality, the underpinnings of the criminal personality are redefined as an individual seeking a universal identity by becoming one with the energy of the physical universe (Schulte).

*

I have defined the essence of the physical universe as energy. Now we should uncover the essence of energy. Physicists and astronomers have made great strides over the past decade with the discovery and observation of quasars, pulsars, black holes, and black matter which suggest time is truly relativistic and matter is made up of very strange things indeed. In addition, Einstein's theory of a fixed or "unsurpassable" speed of light may be, in fact, in error. One of my favorite philosophers, Teilhard de Chardin, spoke of the human dream as being master of the "ultimate energy."

And again, one must appreciate Hegel's words: "Something has vital force only when it contains contradiction. It is a measure of that force that the contradiction can be grasped and endured."

A contradiction exists between the energy of the human affectual universe and the energy of the physical universe. The energy of the human affectual universe and the energy of the physical universe are infinite. For this reason I often use the phrase "becoming one with oneself and one's universe," meaning the physical universe.

Readers may come to understand the underlying nature of the physical universe, thereby better appreciating my choice of phrases to describe such relationships. I also stated that human beings will eventually discover a homogeneity in the laws of the affectual universe and the physical universe. The law is contained in the essence of human energy and the energy of the physical universe in that both need to grow. Therefore, growth is the essence of energy.

Remember, however, the basis of this energy lies in contradiction. Humans must have their contradictions and draw their vitality (energy) from those contradictions. The physical universe also has its contradictions from which it draws its vitality. The best example for this idea (from the physical universe) is the electromagnetic field, in which the energy is created by the attraction between opposite or contradictory charges, and by gravity where mass bends waves which creates energy.

When we observe a human being attempting to become one with the physical universe, a new third space is created. This intimacy between humans with separate individual identities, as described in the chapter "Intimacy versus Isolation" in Section I, is a beautiful mystery.

The contradiction between the energy of the affectual universe and the physical universe is crucial to understand the way contradictory forces synthesize momentarily, generating great energy. But then they must return to their original identities. This principle suggests each force will be more "in itself" than it was previously.

As Edward Chilton Pearce describes in *The Crack in the Cosmic Egg*,[29] "It is not simple fortuitousness that these ideas [of Teilhard and Bohm] were in the domain before people began to 'see' quasars and pulsars. It was the synthesizing the energy of the human affects of many like Teilhard and Bohm with the energy of the physical universe that generated quasars and pulsars of energy."

Although this statement for many seems to suggest an absurd defiance of cause and effect, it is a tantalizing idea because on a quantum level, that is *exactly* what seems to occur, according to recent experiments by physicists. Expectation of specific actions by particle physicists have invariably led to results that confirm these expectations. If one moves the target, the subatomic particle seems to "know" and hits the moved target. It cannot be fooled into following an earlier trajectory. Place two targets side by side and the particle perversely goes through both targets. Although quasars or pulsars are likely to be vastly larger and more massive objects than single subatomic particles, their existence only became possible when science could accept their existence.

Did quasars or pulsars have a physical state of existence prior to this enlightenment of scientists? Certainly, but no one could know or find proof until the concept and idea had first been accepted by part of the scientific community. As science and scientists become more refined, the more accurate and more beautiful does the physical universe become because now they are enabled to see things they never could before, no matter how diligently they looked.

A dramatic news release at the end of April 2012 announced the finding of new sub-atomic particles produced by the Large Hadron Collider. Thus science is getting ever closer to duplicating the state of the universe immediately after the Big Bang. Expectations are that there will be enormous new data developed through the LHC and it's 6 carefully designed programs in the coming years. One I am deeply interested in will be the search for knowledge regarding Dark Matter and Anti-matter. Again recall Hegel "nothing can exist with vital force that does not contain contradiction" As of July 3, 2012 it has been announced that the Higgs Bosom or "God Particle" is only 1 step away from being declared a discovery. Thus now work can proceed in understanding how the universe has proceeded in its evolutionary trail since it's inception.

Teilhard de Chardin[19] saw humankind grasping the very mainspring of evolution. Alfred Lord Whitehead[30] saw nature as a structure of evolving processes, and that the reality is the process. It is foolhardy to try to resolve the issue of who is master and who is servant. If that kind of relationship were present, vitality from contradictory forces would be limited. It is similar to saying a positive charge is more valuable than a negative one.

As sexuality is liberated, so is the energy source, and there will be an ever-increasing development of great intellects and creative minds.

A salient example that supports this view is the general observation that people possessed of great intellect and imagination, living lives of vitality and joy, experience a more satisfying, deeper, and richer form of sexual union. For such people, sexuality is a joyous, enthralling, spiritual experience filled with nuance, delicacy, powerful emotions, and ecstasy.

William Blake[31] writes eloquently of this experience when he describes such relationships in religious terms. Human union is sacred because it is a form of union or communion with God. An uncivilized or crude person is capable of union, capable of pleasure, and even giving some pleasure, but he/she is never able to share in the ultimate ecstasies that more imaginative and "civilized" people can achieve.

I can now suggest a vitality arises from the contradiction between the socially acceptable personality and the antisocial or criminal personality that exists in each of us. This is the reason why psychiatry and mental health do not advance appreciably with the antisocial personality and the chronic schizophrenic. Mental health can help develop a socially acceptable personality. It requires another approach, however, to work with the criminal personality inside each human that is striving for union with the physical universe. Only the astute existentialist at the present time in a society of helpers can effect much balance between these two contradictory forces or opposite sides of the coin in the human personality.

Let's review the five analytic balances. The moment is of first importance. Duration can be built only from a number of growth moments, each of which will have aspects of differences versus sameness; closeness versus distance; unity versus separateness; and knowing versus not knowing. Art and music are the mediums I have personally found most helpful working with these aspects of the personality. To touch the inanimate universe is the key. Then bring in the affectual universe as necessary for someone becoming one with his/her physical universe. That nature abhors a vacuum leaves us with the realization there is always a point of entry, if one is considering the physical universe or human affectual universe.

One cannot approach the criminal personality in each human being by trying to destroy it. We must discover the true direction of its energy working toward its fulfillment. In that way the rest of human nature will gradually come into balance.

To have an understanding of the underlying logic going on in the mind of the evolving universal or criminal mind they need to review Piaget's second or Preoperational Stage of Cognitive Development. At this stage we have egocentrism or belief that the world or universe is created for them and they can control it. There is a belief that all things in life with a common denominator are identical.

This thinking of the criminal mind, therefore, follows the laws of logic suis generis, or laws of identical predicates. This happens to coincide with one of the distinguishing characteristics of the universe. The nature and functions of fields of intelligence or knowledge in the universe are demonstrated in the savant syndrome, a capacity found in a wide variety of people. As with most forces, we know fields not as themselves alone but through the results of their functions or actions. No man has seen gravity, but we assume there is a force we call gravity because things fall to center.

All human experience—whether mental, physical or emotional—will if repeated, aggregate in field effects. These can then act in a casual way, leaving their impressions on our minds, which we, in turn, act out.

William James commented that our reality is merely a minor selection from a vast potential that exists all around us, and is separated from us by the "flimsiest of veils". If this veil were rended, that vast potential, were our brain not previously prepared, would likely overwhelm us.

Through natures's natural ongoing evolution, our brain is designed to continiously screen out fields that have no day-to-day relevance and open those that have. Rudolph Steiner and other "genius savants" could selectively open their veils and access that infinite realm in a highly selective intelligent way, which is no doubt where our general evolution should lead. In summary, the criminal personality is an individual somewhere on that spectrum of evolution unfolding with much of his/her energy focused on that vast energy of the universe that surrounds us all.

It is now necessary to decriminalize the idea of the criminal personality. We should find it amazing that marijuana is currently being decriminalized, but the human beings who use it are not. I am amused that laws intuitively designed for people can suddenly become laws governing plants. Recall my prediction regarding the homogeneity of laws. Some day all human behavior will be first a challenge to understand, rather than first to be judged.

I close with a little anecdote from my 41 years of working with "hyperactive," "bad" preschool children. These youngsters are often viewed as early delinquents and budding psychopaths by some families and sociologists, counselors, and "child behavior experts." Almost invariably, I have found these children to be geniuses or extremely bright children capable of potential genius. I realized early their need to absorb more of the universe, and directed my energies toward that end, rather than using strict discipline or some form of chemical or physical restraint.

These children have proven to be the most gratifying of all individuals with whom I have worked. Naturally, when they are sufficiently suppressed by society, as recent outcome studies demonstrate, they usually do more poorly in a standard value system throughout their lives. In contrast, given sufficient means to develop in a complete and responsive environment—whereby their mental, emotional, and physical energies are challenged, rewarded, and stimulated—their behavior evolves into a self-modifying, reprogrammed state of greater cooperation, less hostility, and greater long-term success adapting to "normal model society."

It is my ideal that a future society will no longer tolerate the concept of wasting human resources, but will accept each individual as someone needed, valuable, and precious to humanity. The sooner human beings treat all people as "priceless," the sooner they will recognize their true value, and the sooner each human being will approach his/her true potential.

The following flow chart on page 152 delineates the contradictory forces each human being possesses, but attempts to explain the criminal personality (universal personality) and the forces with which he/she grapples to harmonize with the physical universe.

Human touch restricts one's experience of the total universe It causes distrust in the criminal (universal) personality.

Chapter 6
Distrust versus Trust

Synopsis:

Human touch limits one's experience of the total universe. To become one with our universe, we must distrust human touch. Unconditional love is the essence of this step, just as it was for trust in the affectual universe. The difference is now unconditional love is our own attempt to master the universe; whereas in the affectual universe, it is the feeling of worth because we exist and our needs will be sufficiently fulfilled by someone. Respect is paramount for the universal personality's need to distrust human touch, and requires increased encounters with the physical universe.

Natural growth in one universe will ultimately tend to incorporate the other universe because the energies are always blending, as long as we do not act as a severe inhibiting force upon the other.

If we are to understand the evolutionary developmental process of the "I personality," or as I redefine "universal personality," we must constantly orient our thinking to the other side of the coin. We have been developing some of our universal personality from the very beginning. In Section I, I placed emphasis on the head side of the coin. In this section, however, I will emphasize the opposite or tail side of the coin.

It is impossible to exclude some involvement with the head side of the coin. Indeed, my objective centers on the way it is possible to develop both sides simultaneously, while emphasizing the tail side or the criminal or *universal* personality inside each human being.

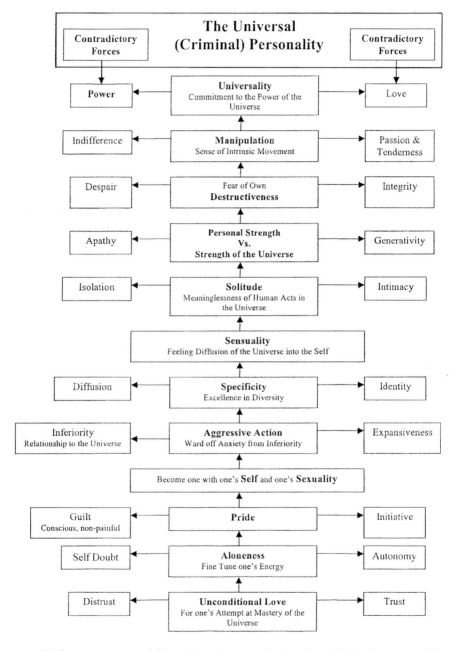

To become one with one's universe, (as in the criminal personality) it is vital, crucial, and essential that a feeling of distrust evolve. There must be an alteration in experiences with the sense of touch. Perhaps the best metaphor I can use is the one from the second chapter of Section I which describes a pebble dropped into water and observing the concentric circles that occurred. It is essential to study the total picture from the standpoint of the circles radiating outward, and from the position of returning to the pebble. Studying the affectual universe in "First You Feel, Then You Know," one essentially studies the human situation, trying always to return to the pebble or the essence of human affectual growth. In this section, I essentially concentrate on the human situation from the position of the outward radiating circles into the universe. Both situations are intimately a part of each other but I have separated them in two sections.

Human touch essentially defines the boundaries of a particular human existence at any moment in time, and to reach out for touch would constrict one's experience of the total universe. In terms of becoming one with one's universe, one must distrust human touch as an aid to that end.

The sublime mystery is that the essence of trust or distrust is the same. It is identical. Unconditional love is the essence of both! The difference is that now unconditional love is one's attempt to master the universe; whereas in the affectual universe, it is one's feeling of worth simply because one exists. It is merely a matter of perspective.

Basic to evolving a universal personality is a keen sense of touch that requires a certain distance or "distrust"of human touch. Animals, especially "prey" that are much more a part of the physical universe, use immobilization when they need to heighten their awareness of the physical universe. Pickpockets or safe-crackers are examples of criminals possessing this trait. The counterpart to this trait is the magician or sculptor—one who perhaps has adapted to a balanced, combined affectual and physical universe—is the magician or sculptor. The blind person or the artist undoubtedly deepens one's understanding of touch.

Examining criminals, I was initially amazed at the way they repeatedly reported there was a sense at the moment of the crime, of there being no feeling of right or wrong, but rather a feeling of total delight in control. This sense can be compared to the love of one's mastery in the universe. As Dostoevski in *Crime and Punishment*[32] describes criminals like Raskolnikov imagine themselves to be Napoleons. From the philosophical perspective, it is crucial to the human existence of the need to move outward.

Yes, there are problems concerning the destructive effect on other human beings. One must, however, first understand the roots of behavior before one can hope positively to deal with it. I will establish guidelines covering the way one might deal with the destructive aspects of the criminal or universal personality.

The most crucial step involves realizing birth and infancy set the foundation for later behavior. A number of societies have spontaneously and intuitively devised certain steps to deal with these types of personalities by essentially incorporating the traits into acceptable roles. It is basically a reflection of the degree to which a society has already evolved.

It is important to consider the role that abuse and neglect play in the development of the criminal personality, because it is a resoundingly frequent and dominant part of the history of many prisoners. Frequent significant beatings by the parent in the first eight months of life incorporate the punishment as normal into the child. Later in life, when the child becomes a parent, the feeling concept of beatings as part of the incorporation process occurs. Thus, later in life when the beaten child grows up and becomes a parent, he/she unconsciously repeats the experience of the beatings on his/her child. This cycle is called "The Battered Child Syndrome."

Brandt Steele,[33] psychiatrist, and C. Henry Kemp,[34] pediatrician, both from the University of Colorado Medical Center, wrote the classical studies of this phenomenon. As a resident at the center at that time, I recorded histories from the battering parent or parents that, at times, extended to several generations. I was again awestruck by another example of the "repetition compulsion" as the underlying dynamic in the sexual perversion of pedophiles, sexual rapists, and murderers. Returning to unconditional love, one can often see it more blatantly in the delinquent or criminal.

A sense of self-love is obvious even to a sneer on the face of the "criminal personalities" who seem to say "My love of self is so great, you can't touch me or it."

Any society has a need, a right, and a duty from and to each of its members from birth onward to know a child's relationships to his/her affectual and physical universes. This knowledge will precipitate great controversy over the rights of the individual to personal freedom versus the rights of the state or society.

Here again, Hegel's quotation from *Philosophy of Law* is vital. It is a matter of perspective. If a positive growth attitude is the principle that underlies law, society will encounter fewer problems. Society needs to periodically assess, from birth onward, the essential makeup of the individuals in society. Society needs to know the importance of relationships to the affectual and physical universes. The old psychotherapy principle of dealing with people from the perspective of their current plight will continue to be valid.

With the autistic child or early criminal or hyperactive child, one must respect the need for distrust of touch and the increased encounters with the physical universe. As those needs are fulfilled, they will incorporate more of the affectual universe. Natural growth of one universe will include the other, as long as the other is not a severe inhibiting or restrictive power.

Although the universal physical personality resides at a later evolutionary stage than the affectual universe personality, we certainly can work with the affectual and physical universes simultaneously. It appears that the criminal personality or the autistic child or the universal personality enters life with an inherent degree of self-love. It also appears to be a form of unconditional love that is unshakable. In a similar vein, one often hears "that alcoholics are the best people." Certainly the Alcoholics Anonymous Twelve Steps conceptually outline an advanced evolutionary growth process while retaining certain nihilistic traits.

I am only lately beginning to appreciate the way the alcoholic is really a type of universal personality (formerly they were criminals) with great self-love. They attempt—through oral ingestion—to touch and gain a feeling of total body grandeur and power for him/herself to feel enormous power over the universe. This method has its shortcomings, but there is importance using one's mouth to "taste" the physical universe.

The key to alcohol as a positive method to become one with one's universe, centers on the culture to incorporate it gradually and positively. The best example is the Jews who have incorporated alcohol into their culture, and treat it positively. It is rare that alcohol is abused in that culture. Jewish culture has an extremely low rate of alcoholism. They have not outlawed the issue of alcohol.

As consultant to Youth Services in Colorado I discovered wayward teenagers rejected human touch. Over the ensuing years of an extensive child and adolescent practice in three separate areas of the United States, I became able to separate the degree of retrenchment of these youngsters through the simple use of touch.

One of the additional interesting phenomena to be noted about the true criminal personality or universal personality is an apparent narcissistic investment in one's body, muscles, and physical health. However, they often destroy their bodies, if they can't synthesize a balanced personality.

This narcissistic trait is most dramatically evident in the prison systems where the weight room is often the most popular facility for convicts. Their narcissistic involvement with their bodies often goes beyond that of the professional body builders in contemporary society. I recall the excitement and enthusiasm of Atascadero State Hospital "patients" waiting the demonstrations of Arnold Schwarzenegger several decades ago.

Closing this chapter, I want to comment on the steroid scandal in sports. How many Olympic gold medals and Hall of Fame records were illegally obtained by "the criminal personality opposite side of the coin," those idolized sports heroes, many of whom destroyed their bodies or died from steroids.

Self-doubt,
experienced in aloneness,
sharpens and hones
one's energy
to tap the energy
of the universe.

Chapter 7
Self-Doubt versus Autonomy

Synopsis:

To enter the actual evolutionary process of the universe and its people requires individuals put themselves entirely on the line. One cannot hold back any energy, yet an enormous sense of self-doubt arises regarding one's intelligence, ability, purpose, and motivation. To fine tune or perfect universal energy, an intense feeling of self-doubt from the position of aloneness is essential.

Assume we are dealing with an individual who has a keen and intense desire to be a part of the universe. He or she has a distrust of too much human contact.

It is quite overwhelming to consider the way the universal person must be positioned to interact with the universe to alter the course of the physical universe and the affectual universe. To enter into the actual process of the universe and its human evolution requires the person to put him/herself entirely on the line. We cannot restrain any of our energy, and yet we are filled with an enormous self-doubt. We begin to doubt the core of our intelligence, ability, purpose, and motivation. In the past we might have felt able to stand alone (autonomously); now we might realize the total inability not to enter into the processes of the universe. Nevertheless, we might feel a recurring doubt of the way or possibility in which we can actually perform our mission within such an enormous, complicated, and marvelous universe.

A human being knows that his/her personal energy is constantly in a dynamic process with the energy of the universe. Humans also have a certain sense of direction about entering into this universal process. The key feeling of energy exists and cannot be avoided or denied; that great feeling of self-doubt exists concerning the actions one needs to take. It is vital one experience an intense feeling of self-doubt to sharpen and hone one's energy before involving oneself with the energy of the universe. The *sine qua non* for experiencing this intense self-doubt is aloneness!

One must literally open oneself to the experience of self-doubt by first placing the self in aloneness. Here again, one can learn from the subtle experiences of the criminal personality. Before planning a major jailbreak or robbery, the professional criminals isolate themselves and experience every possible self-doubt or possibility of error before moving forward. The popular movie *The Sting* essentially captured the fever of that crucial feeling of self-doubt before moving forward.

In the Chowchilla kidnapping, the three men were driven by an inner need to enter into the process of the universe. Their self-doubt is contained in the last diary entry before they proceeded with their caper. This kidnapping was reported in *The Fresno Bee,* Tuesday, July 26, 1977.

On May 21, 1976, James Schoenfeld wrote, "When confronted with a choice of possible freedom and life and happiness or possible imprisonment and life and humiliation, what would you choose?" During earlier preparations, he wrote a tabulation on two sides of a sheet of paper. On one side were ideas of "uncertainties; dull boring life that one would regret in old age." On the other side, "possibilities; goldmine, possible arrest for illegal activities; get rich or go to jail." Under both columns, "Which path to take? Which will lead to my goals?" As Frederick Woods stated it, "We had to try it. Everyone has one goal in life, we had that. It was a good plan. Everything worked good until that night."

In this example one sees the transitional phase in which there is a degree of development toward criminality and a degree of evolution toward altruism. Apparently, some thought was given to use the money to finance projects for the bettering of humankind. Society must realize that the energies of these three men spent over a two-year period planning the kidnapping could have accomplished a great deal, if channeled in other directions. Think of the energy it sparked in the children; the bus driver, Mr. Ray; the parents; friends; community; state; nation; and the world.

There is another scenario that detailed the destructiveness of their actions to the lives of the kidnaped children. A five-year follow-up study revealed essentially a 100% occurrence of post-traumatic stress symptoms or developmental problems in the children. Yes, it is possible to enter into the energy of the universe and affect it dramatically from one side of the coin or the other.

The criminal personality
has a nonpainful
complete experience and
conscious knowing
of guilt while using
the power of control or
manipulation over
another human being
or some aspect
of the physical universe
to enhance a feeling
of self-worth.

Chapter 8
Guilt versus Initiative

Synopsis:

In the affectual universe, guilt is a self-deceptive attempt to gain a feeling of worth by using guilt to control or manipulate another human being. The criminal personality has already decided to move ahead by entering into the universal process of evolution. Deception is unnecessary, and there is the absence of guilty feelings as conceived by society.

The differences between neurotic awareness—including painful experiences of guilt—are contrasted with the fully knowing conscious and nonpainful experiences of guilt of the criminal personality. Guilt for the criminal personality is a deliberate, conscious attempt to gain a feeling of worth and power by using control or manipulation on other human beings or some aspect of the physical universe. The genius, budding criminal and rapist/murderer are given particular study.

✳

In "First You Feel, Then You Know," guilt is a self-deceptive attempt to gain worth by using control or manipulation of another human being and/or some aspect of the physical universe. As society has observed, criminal personalities seem to lack guilt about any of their criminal activities. This idea is true because the criminal personality has already decided to enter into the process of universal evolution. In the criminal personality, no need exists for deceiving oneself through the manipulative use of guilt. Criminal personalities are clear within themselves about their own evolution and that of the universe.

Readers may begin to think I am contradicting myself saying the criminal does not feel guilt, and then say indeed the criminal personality experiences guilt. A very subtle difference exists here, which brings to mind Arthur Janov's[35] differentiation between awareness and consciousness. There is a subtle yet powerful difference between the neurotic awareness and painful experience of guilt and a full conscious nonpainful experience of knowing guilt. The criminal personality has a nonpainful, complete experience and conscious knowing of guilt as I define quilt.

A feeling can occur quietly, knowingly, and painlessly. At some point, it becomes imperative to have that dimension occur if one's evolution is going to fare reasonably well. The mystery behind that statement is crucial to my next major section. It is crucial to understand the criminal or universal personality in relation to the dynamics of guilt.

The criminal is able to make a clear choice about his/her actions, and consciously knows and accepts his/her responsibility or guilt in their actions to gain control of other human beings or some aspect of the physical universe. However, a major difference exists between the criminal personality and the neurotic personality in the criminal personality knows consciously that he/she is manipulating; whereas, the neurotic personality less consciously knows when manipulation is being used.

The criminal does not suffer pain as a part of his/her experience of guilt. Criminal personalities do not see themselves as "their brother's keeper;" only as "their own keeper." The criminal personality essentially takes the position that to leave oneself vulnerable to manipulation is one's own responsibility and cannot be placed on the manipulator. Consciously aware of their responsibility (or guilt) as the moving force of their actions, criminal personalities can, therefore, manipulate other human beings and the physical universe, without feeling responsible or guilty.

This area becomes more difficult because reality would repeatedly tell human beings that destructiveness does result from criminal behavior. The criminal personality says, however, "only if you or society allows it." Society must recognize the need to assist the process of opening potential constructive avenues of activity for the criminal mind, which is operating on another level of evolutionary development; namely, to become one with the physical universe. As long as society continues to thwart this need in the early stages of development of the potential criminal personality, society will continue to reap the resulting destructiveness of this thwarted energy.

We achieve self-worth through unconditional love, through the medium of human touch. That unconditional love opens doors to becoming a loving human being. The autistic child, through contact with the physical universe, unites with the mysteries of the physical universe.

We must realize all human beings, ultimately, are biologically and intimately a part of the physical universe. If human development does not grow positively, growth will shift in a physically destructive direction. Ultimately, the positively directed criminal personality will come to a synthesis of the physical universe and the affectual universe.

At age three, initiative in the criminal personality begins to develop the destructive behavior of the potential criminal personality. It could also be the point at which one begins to see evidence of the "budding genius." A chance may be possible to intercede in the destructively progressing criminal personality at this level of development. Much later than this stage, in the overwhelming number of cases, one is totally too late—no matter the time, energy, or money expended.

The old triad of bed-wetting, fire-setting, and cruelty to animals are good examples of the complex behaviors one may begin to see. Certainly there are many other behaviors in the three-to-six-year-old age bracket. It is important to look for patterns of destructiveness—whether it be to inanimate property, one's own body or the bodies of others, or to other living things.

Hyperactive and destructive children can reach some balance in life, and a few may still become true geniuses. Most of them, however, will either dissipate into criminal personalities or regress to social isolation, hypochondriasis, drug addiction (especially heroin), or into cold hearted politicians, corporate executives, or dictators.

The crucial fact is that initiation of behavior begins around age 3 for these personalities, and, if it already does not have a positive foothold, we might see this behavior as destructive. It is crucial to look for the sense of pain, guilt, or remorse over the destructive behavior. Truly painful displays of affect are evidence of a budding neurosis. Appropriate remorse reveals good balance; no real concern indicates a developing criminal personality. We can no longer fool ourselves about the importance of early childhood behavior.

The qualities that suggest children are potentially ready for evolving with the physical universe are interest and ability in mathematics, physics, chemistry, and biology. Because the sciences deal more directly with the physical universe, these are the ones on which we need to focus.

The Smithsonian Magazine, October 1977 contained a marvelous article on attempts, at Johns Hopkins primarily, to provide arenas for extraordinary genius students, a number of whom went on to doctorate degrees in their teens (Niven).[36] The problems in their social lives seemed quite evident and nearly universal, and it is the difficult arena to which one must attend. The genius and the criminal personalities seem to share similar pronounced problems developing a social life. The genius often seems to drift more to isolation than the criminal, who typically involves him/herself in the most intense, usually destructive, sexual relationships. It is almost as if the academic genius becomes lost or loses the self while the criminal personality refuses to lose the self and challenges the physical universe and those in power to a bitter end.

At this point, the evolving criminal personality will begin to plant the seeds which later can develop rape and rape-murder behaviors. The line between pain and pleasure for criminal personalities in rape becomes difficult, at times, to delineate.

Rapists need to possess or incorporate the energy of the universe through other human beings' sexuality. It is pitted against the need of another human being's desire to be in sole possession of his/her personal sexuality. His/Her entire sense of balance may be at stake. The rage that boils within these criminal personalities reflects an enormous imbalance between the forces striving for mastery of the physical universe and the need for fulfillment of human social needs. If these needs have been severely thwarted, then the criminal personality will strive to fulfill them via force, simultaneously expressing the rage that lies within.

One of the most powerful contradictions in human behavior involves raping and then killing or vice versa. These people could especially be powerful forces in society, if only they could endure the powerful contradictions that rage within them. Beware of the child showing considerable social withdrawal and isolation with an impulsiveness toward material goods and a need to possess them at this early age. We ultimately see myriad variations in body parts that are especially mutilated and demands for various responses from their victims in the repetitive compulsive behaviors of the criminal personality. There is frequently an unconscious symbolism from childhood contained in the behaviors.

The criminal personality's
intense feelings
of inferiority, in
relation to the
physical universe,
prompt a continuing
process of expanding
areas of criminal
activities.

Chapter 9
Inferiority versus Expansiveness

Synopsis:

The increasing need to possess and be part of the physical universe arises from the unavoidable feelings of inferiority in relation to the physical universe. The classical history in criminal activity is elucidated. The cultural aspects of inferiority in America are examined with the health, education, welfare complex looked at in detail. However, as Don Juan pointed out in Carlos Castaneda's works, only when humans ultimately accept their meaninglessness, by virtue of the inferiority process, can they realize the need to expand and grow through learning.

The greater the internal rage over nonfulfillment and the greater the need to aggressively externalize these feelings of one's inferiority, the more criminal personalities need to separate feelings of anxiety from feelings of inferiority. The medium through which this goal is accomplished centers on aggressive action and possession of external objects or people. Anxiety precedes the criminal personality's rage.

Aggressive behavior towards things, animals, people, including aggressive abusive language in four-to-ten-year-olds, are hallmarks of criminality. Potential criminal personalities possess an awareness of their acts. Because they lack guilt and anxiety about their rage, they feel justified committing aggressive acts as a way to realize fulfillment with their physical universe. Their value system supercedes fulfillment with people.

We rarely see these individuals in pure culture as the budding asocial personality, but gradually the courts are seeing more of them in preteen or early teenage years.

I reiterate that a certain level of fulfillment in the physical universe is their goal and will have to be dealt with for them to incorporate anything from the affectual universe. We need to take the so-called mentally ill and provide an enriched opportunity to release them out of their withdrawal. Society will have to realize the need to approach the potential or criminal personality in much the same manner, with the emphasis of enrichment on the side of the physical rather than the affectual universe.

The difficulty is that there is no end point for the criminal personality. The need of the criminal personality to possess the physical universe increasingly arises from the intense feeling of inferiority in relation to the physical universe. This need prompts the criminal personality to continually expand areas of involvement and, thus, an ever-wider area of criminal behavior. An expanding series of steps continues to widen the arena of their criminal activities.

The impact of this idea is powerful, but difficult to grasp. The drive will be lifelong in the criminal personality. They want to become one with the physical universe. The need for society to provide areas for this growth in the physical universe will be nonending.

The next crucial concept in the universal personality centers on expanding. Society has always, out of ignorance, attempted to constrict such people.

The benefits of expanding growth in children are vital to society's health. I am not saying one should allow or encourage massive destructive play on the part of infants and children. I am saying one must strive to understand that part of the universe of which the child is attempting to become a part. We must understand and assist that process.

In my hundreds of experiences with children, they were far

more ready to attempt human affectual exchange. While director of mental health in southeastern North Carolina, my co-ordinator Sandy and I engaged groups of the most aggressive, hostile, delinquent, destructive, preteen and teenage boys in football games until all players were exhausted. Then we sat down for brief moments of discussion Amazingly, they seemed instinctively to "go hell bent for leather" at each other, but respected that Sandy and I occupied a different place and were, therefore, not mauled. At times we were able to have the youngsters accept a mutually respectful handshake from each another—after having first endorsed their own self-respect by pummeling one another during the game.

It should come as no surprise that in the collegiate world and in professional football there is a continuous demonstration of the "criminal side of the coin," in terms of the players running afoul of the law in every conceivable manner—as evidenced by the Cincinnati Bengals of 2006.

The 2012 explosion of a Bounty Hunting Program of the New Orleans Saints under the defense co-ordinator with no objection by the head coach resulted in both suspended for the season. Coupled with over 100 legal cases against the NFL for traumatic brain injuries due to essentially negligence with known data and statistics laid bare the criminal side of the sport itself. Finally 3 player suicides, likely related to TBI's, with the loss of one of it's legends, Junior Seau, will lead to significant rules and oversight designed to reduce the carnage to the players and mollify the social critics. However, the underlying drive of aggressive energy seeking domination of the physical of another will continue, only more subtly. It will be interesting to see if the USA gradually evolves where the less dangerous sport of soccer replaces football as #1, similar to countries throughout the world.

Although basketball is less aggressive, one can see similar trends. The University of Arizona basketball team became enmeshed in a group activity involving candy machines at the University of Kansas. The Detroit Piston and Indiana Pacer brawl with sports fans led to charges against all parties involved. The incident further illustrates players *and* fans often expose their "other side." Society seemingly has great tolerance for criminal behavior within certain societal roles, such as sports, governmental agencies like the CIA, white collar CEOs, and heads of states. They receive wrist slaps at times to appease the populace.

The city of Phoenix, Ariz., stands out as a paradox in that when any of its sports figures, even its stars, run afoul of the law, they are quickly dispatched from the city.

I share another example from experiences in Willmington, North Carolina. Faye, the coordinator of children's services, and I had many poignant experiences with the very young. A kindergarten teacher called in a panic one afternoon to describe that one of her 4-year-olds with a chronic behavior problem could no longer be tolerated. It rained hard that morning and at noon recess the boy sprawled out in the middle of a big puddle and, mimicking an alligator, snapped and bit several classmates.

On his arrival at the clinic, he commented on the signs on the door,"So you are a psychiatrist and a social worker. Why does it say private on the door?"

During our brief evaluation we reinforced his vast interest in various forms of aquatic life. We called the University of North Carolina Oceanographic Institute at Wrightsville Beach, just a few miles away. We arranged for the boy to spend several afternoons a week participating at the facility.

A thank-you call came from the teacher shortly thereafter marveling at the dramatic change in the boy, who was now seen as a delight.

This example, one of many illustrates what we came to lovingly title "another one of our little genius bastards."

Visiting many kindergartens and first grade classrooms in New Hanover County, Faye and I discovered how prevalent it is that frustrated talents or interest can lead to early forms of criminal behavior. We were known for our round carpet we brought with us to sit on with the students, teachers, and interested parents. We evaluated the children's stages developmentally, positively and negatively.

We were initially shocked to learn of the conflict these youngsters already experienced in their lives. It further illuminated the frequency that "tail side of the coin" behaviors were already emerging as a result of frustrations of native talents and excessive restrictions in multiple areas of their lives. In addition, numerous issues of abuse and neglect were uncovered that were disrupting the evolutionary growth of their affectual personalities.

If we take note of society from an economic standpoint and examine the areas that seem to have the greatest cost (or are perhaps the greatest drain on resources), several are prominent. Certainly the criminal personality and the police, judicial, and penal systems are enormously costly. More and more the health, education, welfare, and Social Security systems are drawing increased attention because they face bankruptcy.

The enormous underlying feeling of the vast population involved in the HEW complex is one of inferiority, leaning toward a feeling of futility. The unemployment rolls grow and we become gradually complacent to the increase. Let no one be foolhardy enough to feel people are less intelligent—no matter the statistics the educational institutions reveal about the alarming fall in basic educational skills in today's students.

As the evolving young people of today become more worldly, have more sense of a universal personality, and perhaps have more of a hardened criminal personality, we can detect some emotional withdrawal from the "rat race of success" of earlier generations. They have a growing sense of inferiority in relationship to the physical universe. There is still interest, enthusiasm, curiosity, but they are accompanied by a different sense of one's weight in relationship to the enormous physical universe.

In the vast adult group in the HEW complex, there is an enormous sense of loss in the quality of life regarding personal services, and so-called consumer goods. As the "ma and pa" businesses have fallen to the multinational corporate giants, certainly human beings feel a sense of inferiority over the control of their lives. The responsibility for personal errors or difficulties more and more falls on the computer, which is born of human's own ingenuity. Actually, as human affectual development expanded, so did the human need to participate in the enormous totality of the physical universe. As described earlier, in this way pulsars and quasars were discovered. Hence, the human need for the computer arose.

The human personality (physical universe or criminal personality) in its push to enter into one with its physical universe was destined for a period of inferiority as the enormous complexity of such participation with a total physical universe came into perspective. For a period, great numbers of people, from such overwhelming feelings of inferiority, will abandon the race and permanently live their lives on the welfare rolls. Their feelings of inferiority may be uncomfortable or comfortable in this role.

Similarly, adults who continue to struggle with the expansion of a computer's abilities or young students who can grasp the perspective of the world's place in the cosmos may be comfortable or uncomfortable. The truly powerful criminal personality—politicians of the world— have always realized the necessity of having a certain percentage of the populace on welfare because these people are part of the base that creates their position of power.

There is something critical about this particular point of the human personality's evolvement. Whereas "the silent criminal personality of society" (those in the HEW complex) are extremely costly economically, this drain, in a sense, pushes the populace and corporate giants to expand into the universe with aggressive energy so yearly profits or the gross national product can continue its yearly growth. How beautiful is Hegel's insight into the vitality created through contradiction.

As political and religious groups espouse their great caring for all of humankind, and effectually feel important, they aggressively expand the deterioration of the physical universe's barriers. Meanwhile, the criminal personality in the HEW complex feels inferior to this unfathomable evolving universe, but finds a way to have it support him/her meagerly.

I have been describing an evolutionary growth process in these chapters: the growth process of the evolving criminal personality. It is a growth process and contains meaning, value, and purpose. However, it involves a movement toward socialism to some degree, but unmistakably societies are already in the throes of an evolving world socialism.

As we have witnessed the beginning of the dissolution of the old Southern plantation aristocracies—which, contrary to history books, did not die but grew in number after the Civil War—so will society ultimately see the breakup of the Westlands land barons in California and, eventually, the multinational oil conglomerates. Socialization of the land and other natural resources vital to all humans will occur as currently undertaken by Chavez in Venezuela.

Certainly an outcry will arise that the quality of life is diminishing. The classical example is the quality of medical care and affectual caring suffers greatly under socialized medicine. Only then will people gradually come into more peaceful inner harmony with their physical bodies, and, to a lesser degree, use their bodies for self-punishment or as a means of provoking guilt in others.

Humans, like animals, have always known the way to care for their bodies. Pearce, in *Exploring the Crack in the Cosmic Egg*,[25] uses the phrase an "inner body knowing" that tries to keep humans in touch with the flow of nature that resides in everyone.

I do not mean there will be a return to the family-owned and operated farm. Rather, there will be a growth toward human individuals joining together to toil in unison for the fulfillment of needs that I have been outlining in this book. One needs the evolving criminal personality, if one can only begin to understand it better and incorporate its important dynamic energy into the flow of the natural universe.

Now we can grasp the essence of inferiority truly is fun. Only as one can see, appreciate, and accept one's inferiority in relationship to the total universe can one enjoy and have fun in the universe; or, from the other viewpoint, only as one begins to play and have fun in the universe will growth occur in one's awareness and acceptance of the magnitude of the universe.

Carlos Castenada,[37] in his apprenticeship with Don Juan, finally came to appreciate the need to abandon his great feeling of self-importance. As Don Juan pointed out, only when humans accept their meaninglessness can they begin to realize that ahead lies the need to expand through learning. The prerequisite for this concept is the feeling of inferiority in relationship to the universe or creation.

The criminal personality's intense feelings of inferiority, in relation to the physical universe, prompt a continuing process of expanding areas of criminal activities.

Chapter 10
Diffusion versus Identity

Synopsis:

When one appreciates ultimate meaninglessness of one's life, in relation to the magnitude of the universe, the necessity for a singular identity disappears. Thus, the criminal personality is free repeatedly to diffuse into new mediums. I provide illustrative examples. Vital to the criminal personality is taking a path that has heart and then making every act count. This diffusion process, over time, leads to society's incorporation of aspects of the criminal personality's variable identities. Sensuality is a diffusion of universal energy into the individual, and individual sexuality into the universe. The state of depersonalization is the most well-known and common experience of the process of diffusion, and is explained in detail.

When a criminal personality comes to the point of losing a sense of self-importance and appreciates the ultimate meaninglessness of his/her life, in relationship to the magnitude or totality of existence, there is no longer one thing this individual must be or one identity he/she must maintain. This is not to say the need to continue will not be felt. It will. But whatever form or method is chosen, a sense of vitality will occur. Only now it is not vital that it be a solitary single form or identity. Her/His identity may or may not continue to be vital.

Thus, the criminal personality has the ability repeatedly to change or diffuse into a new medium. The power criminal groups in society know the importance of being flexible with diversification and rediversification. The Mafia moves to the new vice, in which people show interest, which helps create new vices. The multinational corporations through Madison Avenue and Paris essentially do the same. Likewise, the politician is always ready to jump on the current bandwagon issue. As Carlos Castaneda[38] was told by Don Juan, "There is only the traveling on paths that have heart, on any path that may have heart. There I travel, and the only worthwhile challenge is to traverse its full length. A man of knowledge is free. He has no honor, no dignity, no family, no home, no country, but only life to be lived."

We can clearly see most of the criminal personality's qualities are in the preceding statements; and yet, Don Juan clearly pointed out one needed to learn to make every act count. He also clearly accepted responsibility for his death, even if he should be murdered. Naturally, he also saw death as potentially an explosion into the larger universe and that one's actions were vital. When we take a path of heart and make every act count our lives are vital. Only in that way can one enter into and be a part of the process of the world.

At this very point we can draw hope about potential criminals. They must choose their path and they do. Humans are responsible, if they are fooled into thinking some will not choose to repeat a certain crime, such as murder.

Important to keep in mind is the need to diffuse does not occur haphazardly. There is a specificity in the way one chooses new paths or new variations of a path. The essence of a thing or the essence that underlies every contradiction will always be present. The hardened criminal becomes more skillful at the new behavior he/she adopts, never less skillful. The Mafia becomes ever more elusive, but never less powerful.

In part, this skillfulness occurs by entering into the total structure of society. The Mafia convinces society to accept some of its principles.

In the quest for power, the criminal Mafia, multinational corporations, and countries begin to diffuse into society. Gradually, all individuals in society begin to be infused and assume more of the characteristics of the criminal personality.

As the workers in mental health have long noticed, a gradual shifting occurs in their encounters. The "nice pure neurotic" has almost vanished from the scene. The simple hysterical paralysis has disappeared. Instead, at minimum, they see the character neurosis or the character disorder. The evolutionary process continues and the direction for people centers on becoming one with their physical universe.

The essence of the physical universe is energy, and that essence leads to power. The sense of power now, however, is always tempered by the knowledge that the universe is greater and humans, as is every item in the universe, are equal and not greatly important in themselves.

This notable feeling needs to be more closely examined as it applies to the current era of adolescent rebellion and criminal personality development. In the adolescent eras of the 1960s to 1980s, behavior in large measure was self-directed and self-defeating, particularly regarding drug use and abuse. Therefore, society was not as concerned with the criminal aspects of this behavior, unless it involved dealers or major crimes most often connected to dealing. However, in the 1990s and the new era of school violence and shootings, most notably the Columbine incident, society has become alarmed at the prevalence of the problem. We read about the estrangement of youth from the codes of society and the little meaning and importance attributed to the lives of the youngsters themselves or of any life in particular. We also read about the desire for some form of personal power.

As an adolescent psychiatrist for the city of Denver in the 1960s I had many teenage patients from the Columbine area. After the shootings, I was called at my California practice by several parents of students at Columbine wanting assistance dealing with their teenagers.

These parents had been teenage patients of mine in the 1960s and their children were now the teenagers for whom they were seeking assistance. Because I had lived several miles from the school, I knew quite well the culture and dynamics that led to the tragedy. It was not at all surprising that the type of tragedy that occurred at Columbine was in the process of becoming a national pattern.

I have learned in my forty-plus years of working with adolescents and families that little of what occurs is really a mystery. To predict the place where adolescents' next cultural struggle will occur, we need to study their parents' major struggles and cultural responses to those struggles in the five-to-ten-year period preceding the current adolescent population.

We will invariably find some form of mimicking of the parents' behavior during that prior five-to-ten years: The adolescent drug behavior of the 1960s-1980s followed the benzodiazepine and Valium era of adults in the decade of the 1950s. The school gun shooting epidemic of the 1990s to the present followed the "going postal" and work environment shooting epidemic of the 1980s and 1990s.

I had a number of those postal employees as patients and others from various fields who bought guns and had well-established plans. We cannot be naive and think the children in those homes had not witnessed evolving plans.

Currently, with the evolving health care cost crises and diminishing health-care coverage, one has seen adults use all means of obtaining pharmaceuticals, needed or not needed, with warehousing and selling for profit after trips to Mexico or Canada. Society now sees teens selling drugs at school after family trips to Mexico, with the result of experimentation, abuse, overdoses, and deaths. The analgesics and cold routines from the family stockpile (medicine cabinet) are easier to obtain than having to buy drugs on the streets.

I would like to share a pithy quotation I found useful in my therapy work with patients ranging from teenage years all the way through adult life. I had a 102-year-old WWII veteran and officer of West Point who still drove himself to his weekly appointments for marital therapy and who appreciated the sessions. He once said, "In life, first you must become and always remain that person; then you may become a couple, and of course it takes two. Then you may become a parent."

The most crucial step is realizing we must begin at birth, and through infancy, to lay the foundation for later behavior. A number of societies have spontaneously and intuitively devised certain steps to deal with these types of personalities by essentially incorporating the traits into acceptable roles. It is basically a reflection of the degree to which a society has already evolved.

The Jewish people, with their history of persecution and the Mafia with its family code of criminal honor are two good examples with different approaches to the issue. Both have major investments throughout their histories of sensing the need for great power in their universe, reinforcing their survival as a culture by becoming consummate experts in finance and commerce.

The mystery of life states humans are of no great import in themselves, and they need to be flexible to grow. Therefore, we have no singular identity at any one moment. We always have paths from which to choose. And there is always an important identity for each individual to pursue in full force.

I have emphasized the source of one's energy arises from one's sexuality, and I defined sexuality as the process of becoming one with oneself and one's universe. The individual who has reached this point will begin to radiate this feeling in him/herself and in every action. I choose to use the term sensuality to describe this state in which there is a diffusion into the individual of the feeling of the energy of the universe and of the feeling of sexuality of the individual into the universe.

There is also an example of sensuality that perhaps we can most easily visualize in dancers. The two most obvious examples are ballet and modern jazz standing at opposite extremes of control versus lack of inhibition. Both types of dancers have marvelous control of their bodies, and both must dance with a lack of inhibition to achieve the grace and style demanded of their art. The comparison that comes to mind is one of a beautiful doe gracefully bounding through a meadow. The doe has graceful control of it's body while running with a lack of inhibition.

The inability to have the same sense of dedication or loyalty to any particular career or vocation that one sees in an individual who remains for a lifetime in one particular slot is a logical outcome of diffusion. The same will be obvious in terms of relationships and interests apart from an individual's career. It is possible for an underlying feeling of priority to exist for one or more individuals, but it is not essential.

The greatest movement of importance in diffusing is a loosening of one's hold on the traditional concept of living in reality. Reality refers to the outcome of consensual agreement in society at large about the interpretation of events in the universe that will be acceptable and least frightening to the masses.

The criminal personality or universal personality perceives with clarity the physical universe and no longer needs to bid for acceptance in society because he/she realizes his/her inferiority in the universe, and is no longer bound to accept society's interpretation of reality. It can become increasingly difficult from this point on for people still bound to conventional reality to grasp or understand the thinking or behavior or feelings of the universal personality in the process of diffusion into the universe as a totality.

This process of diffusion is fairly common and to some degree experienced by perhaps one half of the populace. I am speaking of the state of depersonalization that has been characterized as having four typical attributes:

1) feelings of unreality regarding the self, body, external world, and passage of time
2) an unpleasant or painful feeling
3) feelings recognized as being unreal and therefore are nondelusional
4) lack of capacity for emotional response, which often causes much feeling about the state of being unable to feel

This state of depersonalization, a transitory state, was highlighted by the books and movies *The Three Faces of Eve*, and *Sibyl*. By definition in the dissociated state, a portion of the personality splits off and functions as a unitary whole.

Clinicians who have worked with many of these people have always seen the likelihood that a character disorder or criminal personality was involved in this process. Various personalities can develop when a personality experiences dissociation, and we will more easily discover these manifestations when we study diffusion more closely.

Don Juan's ability to be a sorcerer and a man of knowledge announces the issue more pointedly. It is obvious that the person Don Juan describes possesses all the attributes of the criminal personality.

Isolation creates
opportunity to achieve
oneness or intimacy with
the universe by
entering into a new
third space
with the energy of
the universe.

Chapter 11
Isolation versus Intimacy

Synopsis:

As the impact of sensuality heightens, the need for isolation from society increases. Many criminals find it best in prison and often return to achieve an intimacy in a new third space with the energy of the universe. An intensified level of unified feelings with thought processes called solitude is the *sine qua non* of the contradictory forces studied in the chapter. An exposé closes the chapter on the way all contradictory forces studied in Sections I and II can become synergistic.

We now view sensuality is a diffusion of the universe into the individual and sexuality is becoming one with oneself and one's universe. As this process of sensuality intensifies, there will be a period of withdrawal by people into isolation. Unlike a somewhat similar picture in the section on distrust, this withdrawal will not occur from distrust of people, but rather from a fuller understanding of people, with the recognition that to become one with one's physical universe requires that energy be concentrated on work.

The hermit or the bum is an example of the criminal personality from years past. Today, one places the more sophisticated title of schizoid personality on these people. In the venerated Diagnostic Nomenclature Manual of the American Psychiatric Association, the schizoid personality comes under the character-logical disorders or criminal personality types.

Today, it is popular to travel to the Canadian woods or Alaska in search of this solitude and becoming one with Mother Nature. The United States was once such place, and then it became popular to use isolated areas of the mountains. The expression that so-and-so "had gone off to the hills" came into colloquial use to describe those seeking isolation.

For many of the criminal personalities, prisons have become the place to achieve isolation from society. As the world has fewer isolated geographical regions available, humans have realized that the universe and its energy, which is its essence, is everywhere. Therefore, any place can serve as a point of isolation, but one cannot think of any place that can afford the necessities of life and removal from society that our prisons now afford.

I predict from 2010 to 2030 will see society try to reform prisons in the same way it has attempted to reform state mental hospitals. Many similar problems will arise unless greater foresight is used to understand the purpose served to prisoners by prisons. Shortsightedness usually only sees the purpose they serve for society.

If we look closely, we will invariably see a greater sense of intimacy in the isolated person's life. But it also occurs in the area of isolation chosen by the person. This intimacy may be a guard, a fellow prisoner, some outside person, or some physical inanimate object from the world. A silence prevails about the ongoing intimacy because achieving isolation from society, one achieves a greater opportunity for oneness or intimacy, which means entering into a new third space with the energy of the universe.

What is to be gained by this isolation? Here we begin to see the abandonment of materialistic drives that heretofore have dominated the human evolutionary growth process. This abandonment assumes many forms: the "burned-out" phenomenon of the workaholic, many forms of lassitude, apparent boredom, retreat to the cloistered monastery, or the one who retires to the mountaintop to contemplate his/her navel.

In its place, we find a more intensified level of unified feelings with thought processes. A quietness with one's isolation or more genuine solitude is often perceived by others as total disinterest or noncaring attitude. This solitude, in fact, is the new form of openness that is the *sine qua non* of the contradiction between Isolation and Intimacy.

The openness here begins to describe the awareness of the meaninglessness of everything that Don Juan keeps reiterating to Carlos Castaneda and that Carlos fights so vehemently. It is an awareness that all usual or ordinary human acts are totally meaningless, in terms of the process of universal evolution.

All humans must experience their humanness and move through the process of their own personal human evolution. However, it doesn't change anything from the universal evolutionary position.

Leadbeater's Textbook of Theosophy[39] clearly describes the way the individual human must experience three lower evolutionary phases before being able to enter into his/her more intrinsic nature, which is a spiritual evolution. All humans must experience the three phases to complete their own evolutionary process, but all acts, feelings, and thoughts are still meaningless in terms of the universal evolutionary process. The only meaning of individual thoughts, feelings, or acts is a movement to a slightly greater completion of the universe's evolutionary process.

Nonetheless, as Don Juan points out repeatedly, it is important to be a warrior, to fight the fight, to more and more become one with one's universe. Perhaps it would add some comfort to state that it does bring one closer to a more joyous flow later in the evolutionary process.

Page 41, Chapter 5, "The Constitution of Man", of *A Textbook of Theosophy*, outlines the seven stages of human evolution. Chapter 8, on the purpose of life, outlines the way humans must first experience a downward arc towards greater materialism for the human spirit to involve itself in the matter of receiving impressions through it. Next, humans begin the upward arc, in which their spirit learns to dominate matter and see matter as an expression of the human spirit. Eventually, humans move toward a unity of mind, matter, and spirit.

I am jumping the gun a bit in this clarification. Because I consider this point of evolutionary development to be the first touching of the bottom in the downward arc phase of evolution, it is best to have a first glimpse of what the path has been and what, in general, can be expected in the future. The remaining chapters of this section study the groveling at the bottom, such as the alcoholic can best describe before he/she begins to glimpse the possible upward turn. I do not entirely agree with Alcoholics Anonymous on its interpretations, but it does have much to teach human beings.

My section "First You Feel, Then You Know," deals with the evolutionary growth of human feelings, or the affectual universe. This section, "The Criminal Personality," deals with humans assimilating a basic understanding and union with the physical universe. In the chapters to follow, we see humans at the bottom of their arc. Understanding it is a necessary part of their evolutionary growth. The next section deals with the gradually beginning upward arc.

The importance is now more clear of the contradictory forces in the first two sections of this book. It is essential each evolutionary step be taken, and the work of each step be sufficiently completed before one proceeds to the next step. We can now see the so-called contradictory forces are complementary and synergistic forces. A human being's criminal personality is a complementary synergistic force with his/her affectual personality, and the apparent contradiction between them, although at times a very real contradiction, ultimately becomes complementary.

Hegel's vital force occurs when a complementary synergistic synthesizing of previous contradictions occurs.

Apathy arises from
the realization one
contributes nothing
to the universe or
another human being.
It leads to an antisocial,
sociopathic, psychopathic
attitude that no moral
is involved with
human life.

Chapter 12
Apathy versus Generativity

Synopsis:

When we realize humans essentially contribute nothing to the universe, the evolution of the asocial psychopath or sociopath, with essentially no true feelings for other human beings, becomes understandable. A struggle occurs in the criminal personality between becoming "burned out" and apathetic or continuing rampantly, as the severe sociopath does in the quest for personal power or strength equal to the universe as the only reality.

At some point, each person realizes the world has existed previously, and it will continue to exist irrespective of each person. Human beings, unless they become creative through becoming spiritual beings, contribute nothing. The most we can do is somehow throw ourselves into the stream. Maybe we can influence others. But somewhere the truth resounds that people will find the thing they seek in one place or another, and our being a part of another life is really just coincidental.

The apathy I speak of here, however, is only in terms of the present situation that people may have had some major mission in life and now come face to face with the fact they are no one else's saviour.

There is, in the criminal personality, a point at which that person can become truly asocial, psychopathic, or sociopathic with essentially no genuine feeling for other human beings. Individuals can murder without regard, and any type or degree of personal motivation is justification for murder. *In Cold Blood* was in many ways a good narrative of this type of criminal.

There is no longer a moral involved with a human life. When one is here, one is here. When life is over, life is over. Only those moments of one's personal existence matter. Existentialism can easily predominate in this type of framework.

A subtle but smashing stumbling block occurs in the middle of this development. The criminal personality, despite this existential outlook, is almost invariably an active dynamic person in that he/she seems to be involved in actions or making things happen.

There is apathy for others or better stated, little or, no concern for others. There is an active dynamic interest in the self, and the criminal becomes quite motivated for his/herself. It is as though the criminal has a strong need and desire to go somewhere with and for the self. Seemingly important is the accumulation and movement toward strength of self, as if trying to match or enter into the power of the universe. The *sine qua non* strives for personal power at the expense of others.

To face the totality of the universe makes it imperative one gain all of the strength possible, and it is obvious to the criminal personality that one can only do it by and for oneself. Similarly, we cannot do anything significant for another person. Human beings use one another, and morals are no longer an issue. We can become a part of the universe through strength and power, not through kindness or self-sacrifice, attributes seen as signs of weakness in the mortal battle with the universe. There may be an alliance for pragmatic reasons, but no real feeling exists for another person and anyone can be "rubbed out" on a moment's notice.

An enormous sense of strength or force will usually be seen in these people. It is as if these people have tapped into the force of the universe and have a certain awareness that enormous strength can be a part of the self. Therefore, anything is possible and any kind of crime can be attempted and completed. The Los Angeles Hillside Strangler[40] and the man held in Florida for more than one hundred sexual homicides are examples of this criminal personality. The amazing thing is the success of these individuals escaping capture for a rather prolonged time.

There is a total apathy or disregard for any feeling or sense of rights for other human beings. If we look closely at these people, we will see that rarely is it the money, property, possessions, and so forth, that motivate the criminal personality. Rather, it is a drive to achieve personal strength, power, or prowess.

These individuals have often been seen to exhibit a psychosis because there seems to be little evidence of reality, awareness, or concern for the consequences of one's behavior. Strength or personal power seems to be the only reality, and nothing else concerning others seems to be of consequence.

This personality exudes an intense drive to do the thing or act perfectly, and such perfection adds to the lustre of the strength felt from the performance of the act. Death for the self seems unimportant, especially when compared to the importance of making the criminal act as perfect as possible. It seems if the acts are accomplished perfectly with strength, then that strength will somehow continue. It appears an awareness of personal strength is totally important. The act or acts in themselves are unimportant, and seem purposeful or functional as a means of developing and practicing one's personal strength.

The only personal apathy occurs when one is stymied or unsuccessful developing and exercising one's strength. Actually, other people are inconsequential to the asocial psychopath unless they interfere with one's quest for strength or if they happen to provide a good opportunity to exercise one's strength. To the criminal personality, his/her behavior is purposeful. If society at large wants to interfere with this behavior, society better understand the purposefulness and need that underlies this behavior. We are never going to alter the need or motivation, essentially. We can only attempt to allow more feasible and acceptable ways for these personalities to accomplish their objectives. Suffice it to say the essence is the need for growth of the individuals' feeling of personal strength, as it relates to the strength of the totality of the universe.

To understand the long-range purpose of this strength requires additional work. Carlos Castenada in his enormous generativity is uncovering this purpose ever more progressively. My work for the present consists of outlining the steps that human beings must experience in rather complex urban society. We cannot escape to isolated mountains of Mexico to determine our destiny.

My definition of sexuality is the process of becoming one with oneself and one's universe. It is no surprise, therefore, that so many examples of rape-homicide are occurring at this time in our society. Only when society accepts physical sexuality and its full impact on life will humans progress and see other kinds of behavior becoming the popular method of practicing one's personal strength. The next step is likely to be sexual, and involve the widespread use of incest.

A fairly predictable sequence of behavior occurs in the human evolutionary process. A society, like an individual, must experience an evolutionary process. Until this century little has been conducted to understand that process. We will come to appreciate the world of the criminal personality is understandable, evolutionary, and somewhat predictable—if we take a different perspective. It is another world of which humans will be a part at some point in their evolutionary development. If humans are to participate in and understand the spiritual universe, it is essential we evolve and understand our way through this other world.

Punishment, including capital punishment, as a deterrent or protection for victims is an illusion. As long as people avoid understanding and knowledge, people can keep their illusions intact.

Isolationism as a national policy was and still is illusion. It has essentially vaporized with societal knowledge of the potentials for strength through nuclear power. We must hope we can develop the same powerful understanding and knowledge of all the people who have lived and will live on this earth. The folly of the United States fencing its border with Mexico replicates the moats of ancient times, and is a form of isolationism.

Despair leads to
isolation
and personal
destruction,
unless an integrity
of the desire for
strength and power
survives.

Chapter 13
Despair versus Integrity

Synopsis:

Helplessness and Despair manifest as the criminal personality realizes the impossibility for a human being to merge with, and become equal to, the power of the universe. The attempt sets in motion a totally destructive process in the criminal personality. She realizes the conception of reality and "the way things go" is shattered, and the struggle to maintain conviction and integrity of one's beliefs may often lead to attempted suicide.

As the criminal personality realizes how nearly impossible it is to merge into the dynamic forces of the physical universe, a feeling of helplessness persists. It then progresses further. No matter what the criminal personality does with the energy to become one with the physical universe, he/she seems to put a destructive process in motion.

The criminal personality must grow. There has been a purpose behind all his/her actions. The purpose has been to enhance his/her personal strength and unite with the power of the physical universe, no matter the cost to others or him/herself. The hitch is the criminal personality acts with the inherent idea that something real, tangible, valuable, "positive in his/her terms" would result from it.

The appreciation of the recurrent destructiveness shatters the self and his/her ideas and conceptions of the way things are supposed to go. The major impact most commonly results in the criminal personality locking him/herself in isolation. The kinds of prisons are multiple. The most striking example of this phase of evolutionary growth in the criminal personality I have seen occurred in the 1980s in Ward 14 at Atascadero State Hospital in Atascadero, Calif., a hospital for the criminally insane and violent sex offenders.

I witnessed individuals who would do all in their power to have themselves locked in seclusion and be placed in physical restraints. They knew and feared their own destructiveness, which they had come to know would emerge if given latitude. Their force, strength, and energy had developed whereby they felt any control or restraint had disappeared.

These individuals were locked in a particular place in an evolutionary process. They seemed an undifferentiated amorphous mass with human feelings and emotions and the energy of a tornado. Having some awareness or insight into the presence of both feelings is terrifying and demands some degree of restraint to survive without totally shattering.

It is considerably different from the impulsive, explosive personality who lacks insight and cannot predict or know in advance when an eruption will occur. Unbalanced humans can exist—psychotic at moments, but not most of the time. Humans can evolve at that delicate position in the evolutionary development of a criminal personality. Usually, these people, at this point, are not actually psychotic. Some of these individuals might have organic brain damage or impairment of some kind. They have enormous primitive energy which can erupt and look like a holocaust of nature.

Perhaps we can better understand how a Hitler[41] or a Dada Idi Amin could occur in civilization. Hitler and many of his cohorts eventually did despair. I'm not sure it happened from a sense of impending defeat as it was a despair that their way of life couldn't be realized. Nixon, came close to succumbing to despair, but did not. He came closest to despair through his physical bodily trials, but nonetheless survived.[23] Amin was insidiously involved in an internal despair with his marked obesity.

Studying these potent criminal personalities, we see an unending struggle for strength and power. The drive of integrity continues in them if they survive. There is quite a difference between Nixon[24] and his steadfast integrity for strength and power compared to nearly all of his cohorts who, knuckled under quite easily, reformed, became religious— except Hunt and Liddy who maintained their integrity from the position of a criminal personality.

Therefore, we again see the *sine que non* of despair versus integrity or loyalty. Nixon and Hunt may have come close to despair in the goals their quest entailed.

The burned-out
individual
is indifferent,
a marked contrast
to the passion of
the affectual and
physical universes.

Chapter 14
Indifference versus Passion or Tenderness

Synopsis:

A feeling of indifference to life and its struggles arises with a sense of despair caused by the inability to grasp the total energy of the universe and the integrity about one's criminal personality. The burned-out criminal becomes lost, but may "turn an occasional job" with little spirit. For those who struggle to maintain a sense of passion, this struggle is often reflected in a tenderness concerning their work. For example, a mob boss in Tucson may be admired because of the tender, almost unnoticeable, yet passionate and successful qualities he continues to demonstrate. With these qualities arises the ability to use subtle manipulation and the most vital sense possessed by all great movers of history: the sense of timing. This kind of personality finds, becomes in touch with, and uses the intrinsic movement in the affectual and physical universe.

This book is a description of the evolutionary process of the criminal personality. This idea is quite difficult to comprehend because everything, as in the chapter titles of this section, is reversed. It is difficult to conceive exact opposites in a progressive, evolutionary way. It is natural that we think of devolution rather than a positive, progressive evolution. Until we develop the ability to think in contradictions, we will never grasp the essence of the criminal personality.

Consider that the criminal mind has evolved to a struggle of despair versus integrity. If we understand the criminal mind has evolved to a despair about grasping the total energy of the universe—but maintained a sense of integrity about his/her criminal personality—then we can envision the way he/she might feel indifferent to life, indifferent to the struggle with the universe.

At the same time, this indifference, if it has survived, will struggle with the passion for his/her life of crime. It is a common finding that most criminal personalities burn out by their late 40s or 50s and become lost, indifferent individuals who may work an occasional job with little spirit.

This burnout lies in contrast with some of the great "godfathers," such as the man in Tucson, Ariz., who retained his passion for work and exemplifies a sense of tenderness in his criminal activity. It is so tender—so subtle—no one can really see him in action, but can only be aware of the success he enjoys with his work.

This success was also beautifully portrayed by Marlon Brando in *The Godfather* several years ago. In fact, this rare quality of real subtlety and tenderness is perhaps best seen in the older, successful warlords, whether they are political types like Roosevelt and Stalin or more overt criminal personalities, such as the Mafia chiefs. The common denominators among them are many. They include tenderness, ruthlessness, and intelligence.

Hitler and Nixon are historic figures who will continue to be studied. Nixon, one of the most important political figures in the 20th century continued to emerge and evolve. Hitler's success ended at the point of despair with his suicide. Nixon's came close with his thrombophlebitis. What could the world have done with Hitler if he had not killed himself or Nixon who died? Would society really think they could have hanged or killed Hitler. Nixon did not go to trial. Would Hitler have? Nixon's underlings assuaged society's need through their trials; so did Hitler's.

One needs to learn something from the criminal personalities of the

20th century. We have witnessed some change in world attitudes with the trial of Saddam Hussein and his execution. Note how in a number of Arab countries, save Kuwait, Hussein is extolled as a martyr and idol. Their energy should alert people to their importance. We need to know the direction in which a world society is evolving. Without being naive, we should realize there must be a purpose in all that happens. Any student of history will realize that the history of humankind, as reflected in its leaders, has meaning. And it does not move backward.

Even the Dark Ages were an important phase in European history. Humankind may seemingly stop progressing for periods, but it has never really moved backwards. Once we grasp the intrinsic nature of the universe is growth, then we begin to realize the importance of understanding all that occurs.

The indifference is an evolving process and progressively headed in some direction. When one becomes indifferent, one no longer feels, and one can begin to manipulate. Becoming one with the power of the universe is a crucial step—frightening perhaps, but crucial! It is an awareness, at this point, that the less one does, the more he/she will see happen.

Only through indifference does the awareness and ability to manipulate develop. As the skill at manipulation evolves, we see the natural emergence of the next stage to greater power. People like Roosevelt, Stalin, and Nixon had their moments or times of indifference and were master manipulators at those times. Hitler never moved past despair versus integrity and, therefore, had to rely on periods of apathy versus generativity. He never became the master manipulator. Hitler accomplished his goals with the brute strength of generativity. Roosevelt, Stalin, and Nixon were much more subtle, manipulative, and successful incarcerating people who might have been a threat. Hitler continued to use brute strength. Patton and MacArthur were Hitler's counterparts. It would be difficult to find anything about which Patton or MacArthur were indifferent! Eisenhower, however, had a touch of indifference and was a manipulator.

Timing is one of the most subtle qualities of human existence. It is the epitome of tenderness, and yet carries the vigor and importance of passion. All great movers of history possessed excellent timing. Individuals who reach this point are almost certain to leave their marks on evolution. Because they are in touch with the intrinsic movement in the affectual and physical universes, the basic growth process that underlies it gives them this sine qua non sense of timing.

There is a commitment
in a truly mature
adult love relationship
to enhance the
evolutionary growth of
both individuals. Likewise,
the universal personality
is committed to enhance the
evolutionary growth of the
universe and human beings.

Chapter 15
Power versus Love

Synopsis:

Section II closes with the criminal personality committing him/ herself to the evolution of the universe through spirituality of a universal evolutionary nature. A transcendence to spirituality apart from usual humanness allows him/her to step toward genuine creativity.

I learned from my experiences at national conventions for hospital and community psychiatry the more distant power separates itself from the place where the vital thrust of activity is in force, the more ineffective the power becomes. This idea is contradictory to conventional wisdom which states power more and more removed from the scene of action is increasingly more isolated and difficult to reach. Only the truly successful military geniuses of history have grasped the need to be as near the front as is realistically safe and possible. These men realized the need to have a moveable headquarters.

An issue rather central to the theme of power, in the animal kingdom as well as human society, is the survival of the fittest and most productive. Triage in time of war or other catastrophe commands life-saving resources are used only for the savable. It is clear human feelings and emotions are not the only factors deciding worth in the universe. Nevertheless, only human commitment to the value of the universe and its evolution leads to these principles of placing the universe and its evolution before or above that of the individual. This commitment to the universe and its evolution becomes a truly constructive power.

The essence of power and the essence of love are the same. In both cases the need to enhance the evolutionary growth of human beings and the universe are immediate corollaries. It is true that once we have loved, we can and will love again. Once we have participated in the power of the evolutionary process of the universe, we commit and make a promise to that process evermore. We must be ever mindful that abuses can occur in the struggle for power and love.

I propose a new concept which will contradict a principle in the first section but set the tone for the next section. Once a human being has sincerely and definitively reached the point of power that can influence the evolutionary process of the universe, he/she now has the ability to become creative.

It is not in the realm of human beings to be creative, only generative. I hold to that principle. Notice I use "individual." For some, soul might be a better choice. At this point, a transcendence from strict humanness to something more than the physical becomes possible. I include few people in this arena: namely, Teilhard de Jardin, Eric From, Hegel, the Greek philosophers, Elvis Presley, Einstein, and Mangione who might have reached that pinnacle. There have certainly been others.

These individuals were able to enter into the universe's evolution through the creation of a distinct new feeling that begins to exert a force. Creating a new character in the universe can be measurable in physical, affectual, and spiritual dimensions. Some spiritual or religious leaders may qualify, but often their influence has limited and inhibited growth in human beings and the universe.

This concept is a preface for my next section on spirituality. I am not using this term to equate the idea of religion or religiosity. Rather, I am using this term from a position of the evolution of the universe or the idea of universality. Religiosity, too often is merely a substitute word for the concept of guilt. The Church has its saints. Hopefully some day it might fully grasp the importance that these people were not highly imbued with a sense of guilt.

I need to emphasize that power, the subject of this chapter, has its essence in the movement of entering into the evolution of the universe creatively. More forcefully, the *sine qua non* is a commitment or promise to do all one can creatively to enter into universal evolution. Those recognizing this universality discard the need of the individual and replace it with the need of the universe. Knowing it does not in any way bring an end to the individual. It combines the inescapable link between the evolution of the universe and the evolution of the individual.

There is genius
inherent in human beings.
Its fulfillment or
lack of fulfillment
reverberates
throughout the
universe and
humankind.

Chapter 16
The Beginning Steps for the
Resolution of the Criminal Personality

The basic concept is genius and/or the frustration of that genius in the human individual fuels the drive for criminality. Multiple etiological factors color this picture and must be dealt with individually. An individual's genius is the compilation of one's experiences, To tap that genius and bring it to fruition, an intimate study and knowledge of one's entire existence is crucial. However, the criminal personality entails a special kind of genius beyond that which many scientists and philosophers believed is contained in every human being.

Society must accept the need to make process studies of all human members. This study is especially vital to identify the potential criminal personalities or those individuals entering into the evolution of the physical universe.

The BTK Wichita, Kan,. murderer is an excellent example. He was able to describe dreams, beginning at age three, that heralded dangerous conflicts. By his early grade school years, he was already involved in criminal behavior type fantasies. My work screening kindergarten and first graders enabled me to identify many children at great potential risk of—or already involved in—criminal-type behavior. Just as science strives to diagnose autism and other childhood disorders early, so must society encourage methods to diagnose the universally driven or criminal personality early.

Society must be willing with these individuals to enter into constructive social engineering similar to attempts by the Russians and the Jews, but under a definite process of selectivity. Society can enhance the positive development of individuals especially attuned to the evolutionary process of the universe by aiding rather than inhibiting the development of this genius.

The following is an outline of the essential steps in my program of reconstructive therapy utilized in work with criminal personalities and excerpted from "Study and Treatment of 46 Psychotic Patients with Convictions of Homicide."

The patients in the study were all found to have criminal personality disorders as a primary or secondary diagnosis.

In reconstructive therapy with these patients, I continually found it necessary to distance myself from the daily work of psychotherapy and search for philosophical support before proceeding. Therapy with patients who have exhibited such a marked degree of dangerousness is an existential commitment. It means taking responsibility for providing the greatest possible degree of security to society and to minimize—hopefully eliminate—the chance any destructiveness will result on release of any of these patients. At the same time, the therapist is committed to the rights of the patients within that framework of public safety. Faced with the inherent tension posed by these polarized commitments, I found Hegel to provide a degree of solace and deeper understanding:

> *"There is nothing that can exist*
> *in life with vital force that does*
> *not contain contradiction. It is*
> *a measure of that force that the*
> *contradiction can be grasped and*
> *endured."*

This maxim, incidentally, was essentially adopted by the therapy group as one of its guiding principles.

Experience over a six-year period with these patients, using combined individual and group psychotherapy, has resulted in a clinical outline of the necessary stages these patients must encounter to achieve successful resolution of their underlying, inherent dangerousness. This clinical outline has, moreover, helped me to develop what I believe is a professional level of security in recommending release of these patients back to the community.

The First Stage of Therapy

After a period of individual therapy, once symptoms had by and large gone into remission, an attempt was made to include the patient in a group with other patients convicted of homicide, attempted homicide, or assault with great bodily harm. This would only prove beneficial if the patient exhibited sufficient ego-strength to sustain listening to others talk about their homicides and exhibited the fortitude and willingness to talk frankly about themselves and their own offenses in front of others in group. Not uncommonly, opening up about their past offenses was simply too traumatic for some. Patients for whom the recitations were too painful, who had tried group frequently, experienced horrendous nightmares and were unable to sleep at night, despite medication. These patients were unable to go on. With some of these men, multiple efforts over a one- to two-year period would be required before they were able to withstand the stresses of the psychotherapy group.

In the first stage of reconstructive therapy, we largely dealt with the issue of one's sense of value or worth as a human being. The key issue during this early phase of therapy becomes that of establishing a basis for reexperiencing one's unconditional sense of value as a human being. Most of these men need to rediscover, quite literally, the very essence of what it is to be human. The patients often translated this unconditional value for themselves in the phrase, "just because I exist." Unless these men are able to construct a solid, logical foundation for feeling intrinsically worthwhile, there is little real hope for meaningful therapy.

The discovery, or rediscovery, of a sense of worth proves to be inseparable from reexperiencing need. Need is the manifold and shifting flux of affectual feelings that others once expressed for them or, in simpler terms, an unconditional form of love. All of these alienated patients had forgotten they had once been loved for themselves. To reexperience that forgotten love meant having to take them back across forgotten landmarks: experiences, memories, and dreams (that often served as a directional route) to recapture earliest remembrances.

One of the earnest beliefs of the author emerged from his experiences with these patients is that, if any one of these men had not ever experienced unconditional love, he would not have survived at all. The experience of touch and being loved for one's self is crucial to life. Any being who has not experienced that vital touch perishes. The very fact that the patient was alive and breathing was certain proof the feeling had and still existed as a latent force within each of them. It nearly always proved to be a startling experience for these patients, when they began to unearth and reexperience some of those lost feelings.

The shattering consequence of this proposition is performance can no longer be considered determining the ongoing, moment by moment, intrinsic value of human life. Man, as much today as in past civilizations, tends to base values on performance or accomplishments. However, as therapists, we come to understand the patient's sense of human value has nothing to do with his performance, but rather with his need. All the crimes that have been perpetrated have absolutely nothing to do with the offender's determination of his intrinsic value as a human being. It is on this new basis, therefore, that the foundation for reconstructive therapy is laid.

The therapist attempts then to reach these patients through feelings—the universal language. It usually requires one to two months of weekly group psychotherapy to establish this foundation. The contradictory forces of trust versus mistrust that one needs in life can be met, then become the battlefield on which the patient must wage war internally with himself.

A group process offers an ideal setting in which to carry out this therapeutic interaction. Typically, weekly individual sessions support difficult work of the group. The major work in the first phase revolves around the need for unconditional love, or the feeling of value, simply by that one exists as a human being. Work centers on the patient's need to recall repressed experiences, as well as on learning how to seek out fulfillment of this need from his now adult position in life, where he is held responsible for his needs.

On enabling the patient to discover repressed experiences, the author is reminded of one patient who recalled going to the doctor with his mother when he was three or four years old and the particular closeness he shared with her. He then recalled it was at that appointment his mother had learned from the physician she had cancer. Things had abruptly changed, and that she had died six months later. All the patient remembered was the blackness and void created by her death. He blocked out completely the closeness that he felt during her lifetime.

The Second Stage

The second stage of therapy naturally follows from the first. Once the patient has grasped a sense of value which he has received as a birthright, the natural path is to want to have a hand in one's own life, to be a participant in that process. If the goal of the first phase was to achieve a sense of value that is unconditional and derived from others, the goal of the second stage is developing self-value. In the Eriksonian framework, this involves entering the battle between the contradictory forces of autonomy versus self-doubt.

The most poignant result of work with these patients was the discovery, without exception, each of these patients failed to achieve any appreciable degree of autonomy, self-sufficiency, or ability to stand alone in the world when necessary—the critical predisposing factor that appeared to be operative in every case of homicide.

Key precipitating factors for murder committed by these patients were the need to destroy or rid oneself of the symbiotic parasite that was felt to engulf the patient and prevent an achievement of autonomy, the completion of the work of separation and individuation, or the attempt to fuse with an object perceived as capable of bestowing a feeling of autonomy.

Homicide, dangerousness in general, is the misdirected acting out of the overpowering need to be self-sufficient. Only by focusing on the dynamic of autonomy with these patients and working with them in the direction of achieving a healthy fulfillment of this human need can we expect to resolve the problem of dangerousness.

It will take from two to six months to complete the work of the first stage of therapy, namely, for the patient to achieve a sense of value. Invariably, it usually requires a year, and for some patients several years, to satisfactorily work through the second phase of therapy to achieve a sense of autonomy. Patients whose problems are compounded with severe personality disorders will require much longer therapy.

In the second phase of therapy, substance abuse or addiction problems must be dealt with, as well as their enormous dependency issues.

The Third Stage

Once the patient has achieved a sense of self-value, the third phase of therapy may be initiated. The third phase evolves from the patient wanting to do something with this sense of self-value. At this point in the therapeutic process, the patient must enter a battleground where the contradictory forces are initiative and guilt. In the author's definition, guilt arises when the patient has attempted to meet the expectations of another. When that has not been possible, the subject may then feel guilty for not having pleased or satisfied that externally derived expectation.

Guilt is the dark side of initiative, the therapeutic counterpoint to guilt. Initiative arises from the attempt to satisfy one's own internally derived expectations. Failing to achieve self-initiated goals, one might experience remorse or dissatisfaction. Because the person who has initiated his own goals is able to weigh the possibility and consequences of success or failure beforehand, he is at least able to accept the shortfall. When initiative is not utilized, and one allows goals to be set from outside oneself, the result is invariably feelings of guilt.

In the third phase, the goal of therapy is to achieve pride in one's actions, which logically requires the patient to accept responsibility for all of his acts, including his crimes and his homicides. Each patient must go through a process of accountability to himself and to the group as representative of society. This requires a step-by-step analysis of one's feelings, thoughts, and actions that led to the homicide, as well as focus on the meaning of the homicide itself. Achieving self-value through autonomy and taking pride in full responsibility for one's acts determine the criterion for a nondangerousness lifestyle.

There are additional stages in reconstrictive therapy, especially in the search for one's identity, necessary to live in society. The further stages involve the struggle with each of the remaining steps covered in Section I.

Special centers like Atascadero need to be developed to aid its adult members develop positively and provide a setting in which periodic reassessments can be made similar to the old positive concept of religious retreats—without the "hellfire and damnation" atmosphere that religion used to inflict on individuals.

SECTION III

The Spiritual Universe:
The Creative Being

Knowledge and understanding
of the criminal or
universal personality and
demented human beings
requires entering into
their thought processes
and the internal
dynamics of the
universe.

Chapter 1
Perspective

If there has ever been reason for humility among scientists, particularly behavioral scientists, surely that reason is their inability to deal with schizophrenics. Just as the criminal personality has always been present in society, so is it true about the demented. How Einstein must have smiled internally while formulating his laws of relativity when he began thinking of human beings. There can be nothing more relative than human existence.

Most scientists, including researchers and phenomenologists, have difficulty bearing in mind that whatever they attempt to study or describe must be relative to something. Anything with relative permanence must have some logical basis to account for its permanence. To understand its meaning, we also must grasp its basis or essence.

Dementia has always been with society. Many people avoid it as if it were not real. Human beings vigorously avoid expanding the barriers of their awareness. However, we must expand our awareness if we are ever to learn and understand the demented soul.

The reason we resist so violently is simple. To expand human awareness, we must relinquish something of ourselves. Why should we want to? What possible importance would lead us in such a direction?

At first it seems there is nothing but pain, deprivation, regression, narcissism, and absolutely nothing desirable in the life experience of the demented. However, a genuine philosopher and scientist always needs to know, to understand, to incorporate all phenomena of life and existence.

Society will not eliminate crime or dementia. People may eventually resolve the need for the extremes of suffering these individuals undergo. The same thing occurred with neuroses, as a result of understanding and incorporating sexual struggles into the societal milieu. No drug cured any neurosis; none will cure any type of criminality or dementia. Drugs might ameliorate the sickness and, in that sense, help the individual and society. However, we can never lose the perspective that knowledge and understanding followed by incorporation of the struggles into the conscious societal milieu is the only route to resolve human struggles.

To understand the human condition, we must exceed the physical universe and incorporate the spiritual universe. Simple to say but difficult to do! Obviously, we have been doing it without knowing or understanding the way we do it or the way humans developed the ability to do it. We could learn a great deal incorporating knowledge from the field of psycholinguistics.

Typically, whenever something is contrary to the preferred sense of something, human beings must denigrate, judge, and declare that entity to be nonhuman to rid themselves of it or dispel it from everyday awareness. State hospitals and prisons are typically as far from our day-to-day awareness as possible, because those incarcerated individuals are contrary to the more preferred comfortable pattern human beings revere as the noblest expression of humanness. We deify a preference, and anything seen as less valuable is easily dismissible.

However, society is stuck with it. It doesn't disappear! Neither the criminal nor the demented go away. In fact, as I have previously pointed out, society seems to be drifting more and more toward criminality and dementia.

A number of possible thought processes can occur. Certainly the demented schizophrenic has a thought process different from the one most human beings seem to use. However, everyone dreams. It has been said if the dreamer in daily life used the same thought process used in his dream world, we would have an idea of the way the schizophrenic or demented person feels as he lives his daily life.

Each human being does, in fact, experience another kind of thought process while dreaming. The thinking we do when awake is called our conscious thought processes. The way our mind works in dream life might be called our unconscious thought processes. Reconciling the two, we try to have both processes obey the rules of one or the other process. Because we prefer the easier conscious process, we usually attempt to force our unconscious process to obey the rules of our conscious process. Similarly, human beings try to force the schizophrenic to bring his/her thought processes to obey the conscious thought processes society calls reality.

Whatever might be the permanent humanness of the demented thought process, we can assume it fulfills some need and, therefore, has some value. We must approach these powerful human phenomena with the attitude that something of value accounts for its powerfulness and permanence.

Two different separate, contradictory thought processes operate in each and every one of us. Recall Hegel: "Something has vital force only when it contains contradiction" and "It is a measure of that force that the contradiction can be grasped and endured."

I call the study of the struggle with the universe of thought the struggle for spirituality. Always there is struggle; always there is contradiction. Human beings have vital force always continuing within us.

Gradually it may become clear I have been clarifying the human condition. Section One, "First You Feel; Then You Know" was designed to reach the basis for coming to knowledge, hence, the study of the affectual universe. In Section Two, the criminal personality, I attempt to look at behavior and action in the context of the physical universe appreciating its importance coming to knowledge of the self. Now, it is important to examine thought or the context of the spiritual universe to round out the study of human phenomena.

Dissociation allows humans
to interact with
the universe,
whose essence includes
dimensions of
past, present, and future.

Chapter 2
Self -Power versus Universal Power
The Beginning Dissociation

Humanness is a process of evolution. The resolution of one conflict must naturally lead to the next logical conflict. In the human evolutionary process, an individual or soul can creatively participate in the evolution of the universe. Attaining considerable individual power is a necessary part of the process.

To enhance our ability to enter creatively into the evolution of the universe, do we increase our individual power or do we submit to the power of the universe and let its power pull us along?

Hegel's concept of contradiction must be grasped and endured. We readers should not forget that to be cohesive, human beings must always search for the essence of any process. To expand our individual power into the universe, or let ourselves become part of the flow. we must accommodate dissociation, a neurotic process when portions of the personality split off and function as a unitary whole. Classic examples include the multiple personalities in *Three Faces of Eve* and *Sybil.*

Psychiatry gradually realized certain secondary gain was always present in the neurotic character disorder, which then became better understood as a vital entity of humanness. Whether these people might have a borderline psychosis was often argued in legal cases. Quite universally they were found to be responsible for their behavior. Interesting, the first expression used for schizophrenics was split personality. The process of dissociation has long been recognized, but the way it fits into the whole evolutionary process has never really been considered.

The truly creative soul is only able to be creative while in a state of dissociation. Any artist can describe the way he/she feels when in this state. However, the way this state is the essence of the universal evolutionary process has never been put into perspective. Only in the dissociated state can we exist in more than one place at one time. From this state of being in more than one place at one time is born the potential for creativity. As we begin to find our place in the evolutionary process, it repeatedly becomes imperative that we continually confront the process and become an active participant. Each human being must discover his/her individual identity in the affectual, physical, and spiritual universes.

Sooner or later, the reason why of an issue must be faced, as well as the "how" (the method). We must consider the "why" of spirituality or universality. Because we are moving toward the concept of the soul and away from the concept of humanness, we are faced with new questions: Why does the universe exist? Why does it persist? If it is evolving, why is it heading wherever it is heading?

Everywhere there is evidence of the evolutionary process. The reason for the existence of the universe, or its content, is contained within its processes. To grow, expand, generate, and create are the processes within the universe. Only when human beings reach the spiritual universe can they begin to grasp the essence of creativity is the core of the universe. To comprehend on an affectual level, we must experience the steps; subsequently, the answer can be elucidated completely.

The ability to dissociate is real and present in human beings. It is best evidenced by the Hillside Strangler[35] or William Milligan,[42] the Ohio State University rapist found not guilty by reason of insanity. Dissociation is a process that must manifest in affectual personality growth stages, physical personality growth stages, and spiritual personality growth stages. Obviously, there can be mixtures of two or all three of these stages. If carefully studied, we can identify in which of the three stages a person predominantly belongs. Kenneth Bianchi, the Hillside Strangler, appeared to be predominantly concerned with personal power throughout his life. When captured, he was in the physical personality (criminal) level of development.

In the most classic cases of affectual personality dissociation, we find the person escaping from a sexual-performance situation and searching for a nonsexual identity in a more infantile position. In the physical personality dissociative stages, most classically represented by the repeated rapist-murderer, there is an acting out of the search for power through sexuality and aggression—regressive and destructive rather than productive.

In the spiritual personality, there will be a dissociation away from the sexuality of the universe with an obvious awareness of the sexuality present everywhere in the universe. If the essence of the universe and of the spiritual personality is creativity, then sexuality must be present everywhere.

The simplest example of this sexuality in certain schizophrenics or spiritual personalities is the state of pansexuality. Psychiatrists created the name of pseudo-neurotic-schizophrenics for individuals who seemed to enjoy being sexually involved with every type living thing from plants to animals to people to inorganic matter.

We must realize in these examples, such as *Three Faces of Eve, Hillside Strangler,* and pseudo-neurotic-pansexual schizophrenics, that extreme stress can produce profound states of dissociation. Many people experience these stages in more modified but distinguishable ways. The truly gifted and more stable individuals promote the evolution of the universe, culture, societies, and individuals creatively and positively. Unfortunately, those with the most severe quirks can cause damage that often receives widespread attention and tends to diminish the understanding of the positive creative attributes of processes like dissociation.

Harry Stack Sullivan,[43] perhaps more clearly than anyone as a result of his work with schizophrenics, simply stated that anyone who had achieved some degree of sexual gratification in a human relationship had achieved a measure of safety or insurance against the development of a major mental illness. The difference, therefore, between a schizophrenic and a positive spiritual personality lies to some degree in the relative success of his/her human sexuality. The pseudo-neurotic pansexual schizophrenic also has greater relative sexual success than the blatant schizophrenic.

The more successful we experience the various stages of development, including all of the various sexual phases of development, the more mature we will be. The more mature we are at this level of development, the more readily and easily we will experience dissociation and other processes. The less mature the personality, the greater the likelihood the personality will collapse under stress, manifest the naked processes contained in all human beings, and develop a clinical illness with blatant manifest symptoms.

Dissociation centers on being able to approach the work from a stable, mature position. Even from a stable, mature position, conflicts occur. They generate anxiety and require will power and strength to overcome. Wisdom dictates human beings conduct a personal inventory before proceeding with each new step. And we must confront all the previous stages before launching into the next stage.

To gain a sense of the process of dissociation and its purpose, we should think about the universe. Individual orientation in life and daily occurrences usually includes three spheres: time, place, and person. For two humans to communicate, it is important to occupy the same wavelength in these three spheres.

If we are developing a relationship with the universe, we must become part of the universe and enter into its forces. We must be willing to do so on the universe's terms and relinquish the usual social human terms.

The universe is past, present, and future simultaneously. The universe is simultaneously all places that have ever been, that exist presently, or that will ever exist. The universe is all creatures past, present, or future simultaneously, including all the evolutionary changes that have occurred in all species.

To experience the processes of the universe and participate in its evolution will naturally require the ability to be in more than one place, in more than one time in history, involving more people. Perhaps we can see the way multiple personalities might be necessary. Individuals with a number of quirks might require more than one personality to return to the different areas of their lives, so they can try to resolve issues which might have developed.

Perhaps we can see the way analysts treat the fairly healthy using dissociation or free association. They allow people to exist in the different places of their lives and allow seemingly illogical associations which are not too different from schizophrenic thought productions. We all use these states of altered consciousness every night in our dreams, which are essentially the same as the schizophrenic thought process or that which occurs in analysis, hypnosis, or amytal interviews.

The individual who has achieved sufficient measures of success in intimacy will be able to successfully use dissociation. Even more, the person who has succeeded in love relationships will welcome the experiences of dissociation. Above all in the loving intimate sexual relationship, lovers sharing the energy of each other and altruistically give his/her energy to the other without expectation. The creativity which is the essence of the universe requires enormous energy that arises from sexuality within the universe. The key to the dissociative process, therefore, centers on allowing ourselves to feel our own energy and the energy of the universe.

Depersonalization
allows human
energy to
interact with the
amorphous energy of
the universe.

Chapter 3
The Process of Depersonalization
Into a Universal Being
or
Manic Depression versus Schizophrenia

We have reached a most controversial voyage. If we look at the processes of dissociation and depersonalization as part of the same continuum, these terms need not seem so awesome or complex. Although, they can be quite complex regarding the number of end results possible.

In this process, a human being goes from having several different personalities to a state in which he/she relinquishes the need for a circumscribed personality. We move into a state in which we can simultaneously be a part of all things, anything, or nothing. Some describe it as a floating feeling, a nonentity kind of experience.

The clinical state in which a therapist may see someone is an acute state of anxiety or panic. Nothing seems real on the one hand; on the other hand, everything may seem to be bombarding that person at a singular instant in time. It is possible for panic and exhilaration to coexist. The role of sexuality in this process is most potently seen in the cases of homosexual panic, although the acute state is less commonly experienced because society accepts, incorporates, and is less frightened of homosexuality.

Some have experienced a state of free floating anxiety or panic and were able to appreciate the enormous energy of the universe. Just as we can appreciate the need not to stay too long in a depersonalized state (to retain sanity or a sense of reality), we might wonder about the way the universe is kept within some kind of boundary, rather than exploding and disintegrating as a result of its enormous incalculable energy. I laugh to myself when hearing or reading about an energy crisis. My goodness, the universe is pure energy, and humans live in fear of its shortage.

This book studies the way humans can be or become, if they can "keep it all together." If they cannot, certain clinical states manifest. These states are not completely negative; they have positive aspects as well.

Consider the contradiction between an acute state of mania and an acute state of catatonia. The middle ground of schizo-affective states has also been richly studied. We should look at them in the framework I have used throughout this book. I will also consider the neurasthenias and psychosomatic or hypochondriacal psychotic type individuals.

Studying depersonalization raises a question: What are the potential outcomes to individuals who experience such a process? Ideally one could incorporate the experience of depersonalization and move forward in the evolutionary process.

For those less fortunate, there are essentially three routes available: discharge the anxiety into one's mental faculties and make it understandable, discharge the anxiety into one's physical body, use a middle road that uses some of each. We might see the development of any one of three clinical states: schizophrenia, neurasthenia, manic-depression.

Biochemists and endocrinologists are gradually learning there is no pure-culture factor. Psychoanalysts are also confronted with some degree of biochemical and genetic involvement. The intricacies of the relationships between mind and body are on the threshold of enormous discoveries. In no way am I attempting to discard the need for many fine physicians to continue their respective work in the realm of the physical or mental world. Crucial to personal and universal evolution is the process of depersonalization, a vital and necessary process needs to be incorporated.

With the work of Harry Stack Sullivan,[44] Arieti's[45] classic description of the schizophrenic process in the *American Handbook of Psychiatry* and Eissler's work in *Manic Depression* need to be reviewed to help put much of this chapter into perspective. The major difficulty in psychiatry to date is all of the work in these fields have emphasized the sick clinical states without answering why these phenomena occur, have always occurred, and continue occurring—although the manifestations change ever so gradually as society and the universe evolves.

Let us study three contemporary dramatic examples of the destructive potential in individuals with psychotic symptoms of paranoia in schizophrenia and grandiosity in mania. Jared Loughner in "The Tucson Massacre", Anders Behring Breivik in "The Norway Domestic Terrorist" and James Holmes in the Colorado "Dark Knight Rising" Massacre have the potential if studied in detail to expand our understanding of what underlies these type of pychoses.

Insight into Loughner's thought processes leading to his destructive rampage is contained in his question, "What will happen when people are no longer able to speak their mind?" The unspoken answer of course is Anarchy, which could be the ultimate outcome of government totalitarianism.

Breivik, for his part envisioned he could single handedly start a revolution to abort the process of multiculturalism throughout Europe. Remember there is always a kernel of truth underlying every paranoia or grandiosity.

We will ultimately learn the message for society behind Holmes's playing out the role of "Joker" vs "Bat Man" as represented by current technologically advanced Police & FBI forces. Holmes taunting of them with his booby trapped apartment gives us hints at his message. Holmes with his background as a PhD candidate in the Neuro Science of Human Behavior epitomizes the subtitle of this book "Becoming A Creative

Human Being versus Developing A Criminal Personality".

Imagine what outcome may have transpired for these 3 individuals if they had gone the direction of becoming creative human beings in a positive manner. Fortunately all three are alive, unlike previous mass murders, and hopefully will at some point allow intensive study of their lives. I would personally encourage their review and commentary of this book.

The challenge, of course is early identification and positive intervention in these individuals. Clearly the necessary signs were evident and recognized all 3 of these individuals. Society needs to develop the will and courage to step forward in a logical and constructive manner.

From a pragmatic viewpoint, it is logical that the manic-depressive state is the most treatable and, whether treated or untreated, often has the best end result. Because manic-depressive people have been able to use their physical and mental faculties to discharge the energy or anxiety of depersonalization, there is less profound incapacitation or deterioration. It is not too surprising that some of these individuals choose to forego medication because they highly value the enormous energy they are able to experience in direct productively. In many respects, psychotic people and criminal personalities are individuals at a potentially more advanced stage of human and universal evolution. As yet, they do not have it all together.

Psychiatric efforts should be focused on people in the stage where they are (the first principle theory). We must include rather than discard the processes we observe. The television work "Rising Sun" about an autistic child was a beautiful demonstration of this principle. When the mother finally sat down and rocked with him and entered into his physical world he was willing to incorporate himself into her world.

We must look a bit further into sexuality as it applies to depersonalization and the enormous underlying energy present in this state. In the depersonalized state, all energy can become amorphous; sexuality in the universe is also amorphous. It is not absent but revolves much more around the self because the self is a part of the entire universe.

The gay liberation, lesbian and transgender movements want to eliminate sexual repression. From them a beginning awareness arises that many alternatives are possible in the sexuality of the universe, just as scientists have known studying the plant and animal realms of the universe. Indeed, there is an enhanced artistry and creativity in many of these individuals who have been able to repeatedly experience depersonalization. The symptoms of the manic, the schizophrenic, and the neurasthenic have always shared the common component of being global in some way, at some points in time. As we deal more and more in universal language, we will see their symptoms involve more and more of the universe.

A human universal
identity aligned with the
amorphous energy of
the universe promotes
creativity (when
"held together")
or psychosis as
its contradiction.

Chapter 4
Establishing One's Universal Identity
versus
Ideas of Reference, Hypochondriasis,
or
Grandiosity and Mania

The universe has its own depersonalized state and a more defined realistic state with boundaries. As the depersonalized soul blends into the amorphous state of the universe, a natural process of attraction or affinity occurs. The various principles that govern the attraction of bodies or souls cannot be studied here because the volume is enormous. Of importance is natural processes of affinity exist in the universe. Some affinities operate more productively and others less, depending on the relative evolutionary position of each particular body or soul. As the depersonalized soul becomes aligned with some particular and special part of the universe's evolutionary process, an identity begins to form. The continuum might yield an artist or spiritual leader drawn to the affectual universe, a physicist or mathematician to the physical universe, and a philosopher to the intellectual or spiritual universe.

The essential difficulty in the psychotic process is the inability to retain some level of one's personal identity that is singular and not part of the universal amorphous state. When our singular reality does not stand up but results in an overidentification with the amorphous universal state, we see ideas of reference in the schizophrenic, hypochondriasis in the neurasthenic, or grandiosity in the manic-depressive.

The schizophrenic literally thinks everything in the universe has reference to him/her. The neurasthenic feels that all parts of his/her body is undergoing some form of deterioration due to universal processes. The manic feels that he/she has the unlimited ability as if he/she contained all of the energy of the universe within the self.

Those in psychiatry and psychology are well aware there is always a kernel of truth in any delusion. There are elements of truth in the ideas of reference, hypochondriacal physical signs, and the grandiose feeling of energy in the manic. Furthermore, the manic at times has the marginal ability to "hold it all together" with occasional enormous feats of energy. The experience of the inhuman feats of energy released by PCP provides an inkling of the enormous potential of universal energy into which the psychotic individual can tap, when in a depersonalized state with the amorphous state of the universe. Carlos Castenada's works involving Don Juan explore the area I am trying to depict.

In a more positive vein, artists, writers, physicists, and others experience an almost limitless sense of energy when deeply involved in their work. They can continue endlessly without sleep or food. Because it is difficult to reach a positive depersonalized state, these individuals often work for hours uninterrupted to a point of near exhaustion to gain the most productivity from each precious moment.

The most thrilling aspect of following the work of a creative soul is seeing the way his/her artistry continues to evolve in scope, character, material, and feeling. Little by little, more of the secrets of the universe become known and a kind of intimacy develops. Perhaps music and the world's great musicians are the best examples of the way the universe and the soul begin to blend as one. There is music everywhere in the universe, although audible only to those who have reached a spiritual intimacy with the energy of the universe. For many psychotic souls music is their one point of retreat, peace, and oneness or wholeness.

Symbols are the best
possible description of a
spontaneous experience
that is as yet
unknown or incapable
of being known
or understood.

Carl G. Jung

Chapter 5
Universal Symbols

A great deal of study and discourse is available about the existence, purpose, and meaning of symbols. I want to put symbolization into an evolutionary perspective. Jung defines symbols as the best possible description of a spontaneous experience as yet unknown or incapable of being known or understood. We have been progressing to understand and experience the enormous energy of the universe and see some of the effects in overt symptoms (or symbols) that can occur as a result of universal energy. To that end, we must try to conceptualize this process of symbolization and the way it works.

An universal state occurs in which the one constant is energy. This state of enormous energy, basically amorphous and undirected or structured, is essentially sexually generated. Its contradiction is order, and it has dimensions of femaleness and maleness. It has existed, and will exist, for all time.

This amorphous state, and the initial movement toward seeking an identity by this enormous energy, is where universal symbols come into play. This process must be grasped and understood to formulate a working practical concept about any individual's symbolic system or process. Individuals always seek a universal identity connected to their symbolic process. Any one person may be at any particular level of his/her evolutionary development; the particular symbol might provide some key to the state at which a person might be. Therefore, it is common to see a compulsive symbol change from time to time.

My refrain "Sexuality is the process of becoming one with oneself and one's universe." can also be applied to the universe and its sexuality. The themes in life are recurrent and the evolutionary processes have a recurrent refrain. It is not surprising universally common and repetitive symbols have evolved.

However, a most potent and dynamic principle is about to unfold as a corollary to this world of universal symbols. Its implications are quite far reaching, particularly in terms of understanding the schizophrenias or spiritual personality.

A process of enormous energy seeks an identity or direction. It is energy in action. This energy consists of many directions and various activities that will have a common thrust or intention seeking purpose or general identity or goal. This identity leads to the principle of identical predicates, the cornerstone of *logic suis generis,* the hallmark of the schizophrenic.

To understand the schizophrenic's thought processes, we must have the ability to become depersonalized, enter into the amorphous state of universal energy, and align ourselves with the symbolic process of identical predicates ongoing in a particular schizophrenic or spiritual personality. It can be much more stimulating to become involved with an intact spiritual personality that "has it all together" more than a schizophrenic who has uncovered the potential but does not yet "have it together." The principle underlying the thought processes in the two are similar. This amazingly beautiful form of logic can uncover aspects of the universe that remain closed to those who use only Aristotelian logic.

A logic also exists in the world of symbols: a logic to the thought process of the schizophrenic, and a logic to the mind of the spiritual personality. All revolve around the laws of energy seeking the further evolution of the universe. The laws of identical predicates are expressed through symbols.

Borrowing extensively from Pearce's *The Biology of Transcendence,* pp 64-73, we must now study the most dynamic symbolism ongoing throughout history. The heart has been the symbol for the feeling of love and the source of never ending attempts in music, art, poetry, and books, to name but a few venues, to understand the most desired yet elusive force in life. It has remained, as Jung eloquently defined, the best possible description of a spontaneous experience that we have essentially remained incapable of knowing or understanding.

Neurocardiology, exploring the brain in the heart, has opened a much needed dramatically new arena. It makes available new knowledge for an ultimate understanding of love and its potential for the human race and the universe.

In human embryonic and fetal development, formation of a rudimentary heart comes first, followed by formation of the brain, and finally the body. Long before our four-chambered heart, our rudimentary heart furnishes the electromagnetic field that surrounds the embryo. This electromagnetic energy is the first of our heart's triple characteristics. In some clinical studies, the heart has produced an eletrocardiographic trace 3-6 feet itself. It was identical to the one produced with electrodes on the heart's surface. The heart has access to all electromagnetic activity ongoing in the universe, which has been demonstrated to influence the heart's electromyographic tracing.

We now know 65% of heart cells are neural cells like those making up our brain. Our heart, through its neural network, maintains an intricate dialogue with our brain, body, and world at large. Selecting from the hierarch of available universal fields, it transmits electromagnetic information needed for any particular experience. Through its heart-brain-body neural network, the heart sends information to the brain throughout the body. After all the information has been synthesized, the network reverses its flow and the heart translates back into the hierarchy of fields of the universe our individual response to the reality we experience.

Restating the first of the heart's triple characteristics, its electromagnetic activity radiation saturates every cell, DNA molecule, and helps determine their function and destiny. Second, our neuron-laden heart has myriad connections with the body; and direct, unmediated neural connections with the emotional structure of the brain (from which comes the new and popular subject of emotional intelligence, our brain's translation of that nonverbal gestalt type of knowing: heart intelligence).

Our heart certainly has an intelligence, though this calls for a new definition to differentiate it from cerebral intellect. The heart's intelligence is not verbal, linear or digital; rather, a holistic capability that responds to the interests of well being. It continually sends to the brain's emotional system intuitive prompts for appropriate balance.

Brain intellect can function independently from the heart—that is, without intelligence. It can block our heart's more subtle signals. Heart intelligence is not anything of which we are aware, though we surely are aware of its results. The heart has a hormonal effect on the brain. In a cover story of *Scientific American*, titled "The Heart as an Endocrine Gland", Roger et al discovered the atrium of the heart produces ANF, a hormone which modulates and influences the functions of the emotional-cognitive system. Other heart-generated hormones have since come to light, such as tranquilizers to keep us in balance and harmony.

The heart is intimately connected with every facet of the body and brain through its neural extension. The intelligence of the heart, not the intellect of the brain, has to contend with those signals from the pancreas, liver, and spleen to maintain order. Drawing from the heart-to-brain transmissions our emotional-cognitive brain makes moment-by-moment qualitative evaluations of our experience of the world structure, some of which we initiate in our high cortical areas and others form automatically and instinctually in the old mammalian brain. Our positive and negative signals of the moment are sent moment by moment to the heart.

The heart has no structure for analyzing the context, nature, details, or logic of our emotional reports. It responds to the reports as basic facts. In response to negative signals, the frequency realm of the heart drops from coherent to incoherent. This is a survival maneuver that opens the heart spectrum to a variable state. In this fluid state our body, brain, and heart can respond in new ways to an emergency, if the old survival responses initiated by our lower brain systems are insufficient.

In most issues of survival our thinking, judgment, and perception are altered in the interest of defense, with the forebrain locking in to the hind brain's instinctual automatic archaic rapid response. In the opposite experience of harmony and love, the slower more reflective electromagnetic waves allow the prefrontals, through its connections to the heart and emotional-cognitive brain, to creatively think and find new solutions allowing transcendence to occur.

In *Biology of Transcendence*, Pearce outlined how, after more than 30 years of research, Heartmath Institute in Boulder Creek, Calif. developed a program of training that can bring heart and brain into synchrony. Its approach is based on the neurocardiology discussed, and is eminently practical. Heartmath has lifted "thinking in the heart" from the confines of poetry and myth, which have not changed human nature, into the realm of biology, which *can* change human nature. Heartmath's program can free us from the survival defenses of our archaic brain structures and open us to higher heart frequencies. It embodies in its steps the entire premise of Pearce's book: We are indeed made to transcend.

Here is Heartmath's six-step "mind tool" called Freeze Frame. The maneuver can be performed quickly and automatically, once learned and practiced diligently and sufficiently. Begin with less important, incidental events rather than the major ones, which require more muscularity than we are likely to possess at first. As we discover the effectiveness of the procedure, we are ready to take on larger challenges. Heartmath's most ardent customers at its many training programs seem to be corporate people who find that entrainment pays off on most mundane, monetary levels.

1. Recognize when a stressful event is shaping up or taking place and "freeze the frame" at the instant of recognition. Freeze your state of mind, making no mental response. Blank out inner chatter and ordinary reaction for a few seconds and perform the next step.

2. Shift your attention to the area of your heart.. Focus your attention there for the few seconds you will need for step three.

3. Recall a positive, joyful, fun filled event in your life, or bring to mind some person whom you love fully or savor in memory. Hold on to that joyful feeling or image of the person without shifting your concentration from your heart area.

4. Keeping your focus on your heart, open to your intuition and common sense and, with utmost sincerity, ask your heart what would be the best response you could make to the situation at hand. What behavior on your part would be most effective to resolve the tension or heal the rupture in the relationships?

5. Listen to what you hear or feel as your heart's response.

6. Act on the heart's response

Before recorded language was available, symbols were used in the form of pictures. These symbols were based on activity or action, affect or feeling. Both can ultimately be reduced to a sense of motion, movement, or energy. As human developed more sophisticated knowledge, Aristotelian logic and the logic of identical subjects evolved. The logic of Hegel is concerned with motion, energy, contradiction, and vital force, and is the counterbalance to Aristotelian logic.

Aristotelian logic
is to humanness
as logic suis
generis is to
spiritualism.

Chapter 6
The Universal Thought Process

Human beings deal with the contradiction of humanness versus spiritualness by emphasizing one to the exclusion of the other. This contradiction in life extends to the point that human beings are driven by two separate forms of logic or internal energy. In its most simplified form, the pragmatist adheres to reality while the psychotic adheres to spirituality. They refer to one another as nonreality or nonspiritual.

The early spiritual writings bequeathed to modern society are written in the Bible in the form of prophecy and revelation. They are essentially communications obeying the laws of identical predicates. That is why they anger the realist and seem utterly intelligible to many others. The popular book and movie *The Late Great Planet Earth*[47] attempt to bridge the two forms of logic, which cannot be accomplished wholly from one side of the coin.

The major criticism of prophecy and revelation centers on their limitless interpretations. Whenever we deal with predicates, an almost limitless number of factors can become attached to any particular issue.

Human beings are one universe, and everything and everyone may be connected to any activity or energy in the universe at one particular moment. This connection can be seen in the loose associations of schizophrenic thought. Anyone or anything connected to a particular energy or predicate can logically enter a person's thought processes. Even one energy may be connected to any other form of energy in the universe, and therefore can logically follow one another in human thought processes. Dreams provide innumerable concrete personal examples.

It is not surprising, as society moves gradually in its evolution, there is a general increased interest in parapsychology, mysticism, cultism, and so on. By the same token, people who allow themselves to experience the energy of the universe can experience events that belie the laws of space and time and person.

This is a common way ambivalence in the schizophrenic develops. We have an ability to have contradictory feelings simultaneously. If we can be in different places at different times, and one energy can be connected to opposite subjects, then it would evidence the occurrence of ambivalence. The four classical A's of schizophrenia—inappropriate affect, autism, looseness of association, and ambivalence—are usually considered ominous. They are actually requirements and necessary outcomes for the existence of a spiritual personality. Blunt affect or inappropriate affect are simply a demonstration of the feeling connected to one of many elaborations of a particular energy or predicate. If we could enter the *logic suis generis* system with a schizophrenic, we could identify the energy or affect to which it is connected. Affect, in the true sense, never lies and is always appropriate if it remains in touch with the system in which it is operating.

Autism is simply a description of an individual's involvement with the universe in contradiction to involvement with an isolated instance, person, or incident of the universe. To learn about the universe, find the autistic individual and attempt to enter his/her arena of involvement. Is it possible to synthesize all of the ideas and concepts in this voluminous work? Can all of us have the potential to incorporate the enormousness of our universality?

One of the most central questions our American society faces after more than 200 years is why there has been such a dearth of truly creative members in the richest, most advantaged society in recorded history. Repression rather than enhancement of creativity has somehow pervaded our American scene.

Our society is at increasing risk of losing its way in a now rapidly evolving world society. Whereas to date we have been preoccupied with the promotion of genius in the scientific technological area, we now need increased numbers of creative individuals in the humanities.

More than 35 years ago Maslow stated, in *The Farther Reaches of Human Nature*, "Today everything seems to be changing; international law is changing, politics are changing, the whole international scene is changing. People talk with each other in the United Nations from across different centuries." Again he talked of trying to make ourselves into people who don't need to staticize the world, who are able to confidently face tomorrow not knowing what's to come, not knowing what will happen, with confidence enough in ourselves that we will be able to improvise in any situation which has never before existed.

This means a new type of human being. Heraclition, you might call them. The society which can turn out such people will survive; the societies that cannot turn out such people will die.

I challenge to the American Academy of Psychiatry & Law and the American Academy of Child Psychiatry to encourage creativity rather than prescribe drugs for "diagnosed illnesses" To go forward as specialists in the advancement of children and human beings, we must encourage creativity in the nation's young. To do otherwise perpetuates the blindness of our floundering society, and ours will be a case of the blind leading the lame. At times we must be willing to criticize ourselves harshly as a means of disrupting complacency. Great talent lying dormant like an unstruck match needs to be lit at a level that at least parallels its potential and degree of dormancy. Once attention has been gained and the spark kindled, we must tend to the flame of brilliance. To date, our blindness has kept us from knowing where, how, when, and with what kindling to feed the flames of creative potential in ourselves and those we serve.

How many of us look for the point of contradiction in our patients? How many of us look for the point of explosiveness in the people who come to us? How many look for the razor's edge? How many are familiar with Hegel, "No thing in life can exist with vital force that does not contain contradiction. It is a measure of that force that the contradiction can be grasped and endured." How many of us dare to conceive of a goal in therapy to find the point of greatest contradiction and bring that point to the fore?

Of course, that means exposing people to primary process material. I endorse uncovering the primary process with secondary process work. Arieti's work on creativity exposes the need for primary process, but how many of us risk promoting these concepts?

We must look critically at programs for at-risk youth. Begin a task force to study and promote childhood creativity.

It is extremely relevant and pertinent that these three specific groups be the spearhead for this task. We need certain advancements in the legal and governmental arenas involving child psychiatry, if progress is to be made. The American Academy of Psychiatry & Law must be the advocate for child psychiatry in this movement. The American Academy of Child Psychiatry must be the torch bearer, because tapping into primary process material will be a necessary step to promote creativity.

This difficult concept is not new. It has been attempted in a number of places in the United States in the past and discontinued, because it invades several sacred arenas of American life. For example, some groups within mental health structures have broadly assessed the psychological development of children only to run into rebellion of any mental health classification of children essentially asymptomatic.

On the other end of the spectrum, sociological and criminal justice groups have studied juvenile delinquency and criminality prediction. The cry that social engineering is around the corner has usually aborted these endeavors. The major difficulty has been the negative connotation associated with these projects.

Many would be quick to point out further difficulties. The mentally gifted programs for minors in our school system, which at first glance seem to be a prototype of my proposal, are evaluated with a good deal of skepticism. Rarely, however, have these programs really placed creativity as the focal point of their goal—although it might have been lurking somewhere in their hoped-for results.

I propose a clear-cut genuinely constructive attempt to define positive qualities that offer enhancement to lives of our children and, ultimately, to society. I draw from a rich varied clinical background: as a consultant for youth services in one state; initiator and first director of an adolescent treatment program in the drug era of the 60s; director of a four-county mental health program in a second state; director of youth and community services in a third state; and private practices in three states, which at one point included fourteen office-age-related groups a week, ranging from kindergarten to elderly retired. From these experiences, I developed certain notions over the years.

First, my patients derived greatest satisfaction, as did I, when the focus of therapy shifted from symptoms to their true native talent and potential. This approach came out of a very powerful experience with adolescents in reform schools, juvenile halls, and other similar settings. There was a vast conglomerate of neurotic symptoms and varying levels of characterological lacunae. The thought of treating then with traditional defense-and-resistance analysis therapy models made my head swim. There had to be another route.

The magnitude of energy these youths possessed—with an unbelievable, at times beautiful, cunning in their individualistic struggles with mastery—continually amazed me. I confess they often brought disquieting degrees of pleasure. It began to dawn on me that there must lie the key—that what really differentiated them from the many upper middle-class youths in my practice was their freedom to dip into primary process ideation, especially affects which were simultaneously narcissistic and, amazingly, potentially creative. Premature superego consolidation may be potentially hazardous to our youth when the breadth and depth of life is a primary consideration.

I rapidly transformed my approach to emphasize primary process affects, interests, and talents in diagnostic interviews. A process of simple imagery was developed to aid those who already had barriers that interfered with direct access to the material. The results were quite astounding and, unfortunately, it has been only my own barriers that have kept this knowledge encapsulated within me.

All human beings in a free society have the right to an opportunity to discover their inherent talents. Certainly, if we are approaching the point in our society of accepting opportunity for good health and health care as an inherent right or entitlement, then this proposition would seem to be a priority.

Before moving on too quickly, we need to address the destiny of the neuroses and characterological defects, if we are to take an approach with children that is directly positive-growth oriented. In this regard, Arieti in his work *Creativity—The Magic Synthesis*, has pointed out the many creative geniuses in history who have indeed manifested all types of neuroses, psychoses, and psychopathologies.

As Barron also stated in *The Study of Lives*, essays on personality in honor of Henry A. Murray, "Nevertheless, it is clearly true that the creative individual is able to find hints of emerging form in the developmentally more primitive and less reasonably structured aspects of his own mental functioning. This refusal to be content with the basic and immediately adaptive perceptual constancies leads at times in creative persons to real psychological Imbalance."

It may indeed be impossible to obviate those occurrences, but again drawing on years of experience, the net effect seems to have been that those symptoms were much more readily accessible after foothold in spiritual (meaning universal) or primary process identity was established.

A periodic assessment of a child's innate talents is an inherent right, presently essentially repressed and denied by our society. The key to this assessment, I maintain, is tapping primary process affects, ideation, and behavior.

Creativity, to be fruitful, must become a process. It requires an ebb and flow between dissociation, depersonalization, and diffusion on the one hand and differentiation, discrimination, integration, and structuring on the other. As Frank Barron beautifully emphasized, "The concepts of discipline, responsibility, and committed, enduring attention are all too often left out in descriptions of the creative process, simply because what so often first impresses us in the personality of the creative artist is the unconventiality, self-assertiveness, independence of judgment, impulsiveness, a skipping wit, and a tendency to take lightly what most of the rest of us are wont to take seriously."

The following case examples are offered for illustration of my work in this arena.

1) A 16-year-old extremely bright white male was referred by juvenile court after numerous appearances for grand theft auto and prior repeated unsuccessful attempts at therapy. Four known offenses expanded to 30-plus offenses with vehicles usually being demolished.

Imagery work produced desire for a business of his own which he was successfully operating within three months of release from custody. Subsequently, his 19-year-old drug addict brother, 15-year-old delinquent runaway sister, 45-year-old chronically depressed mother, 47-year- old marginally successful stepfather were all seen in a similar manner with major shifts in identity success. A 17-year-old sister was encouraged by the family to seek treatment, came one time, and decided she was quite comfortable in her position of barely passing in school. She was not interested in becoming emancipated from the home. All other members of this talented family were.

2) A 15-year-old very bright male was referred by juvenile court after many appearances with a history of incest with his 40-year-old divorced mother and 18-year-old sister. He had offenses of dealing in drugs, school dropout, breaking and entering, and larceny. Imagery work produced a desire for superiority in athletics, which he had never attempted competitively. Results involved a return to school with excellence in athletics and academics. Mother was similarly treated with establishment of a career for the first time in her life. His sister was treated for delinquency, school phobia, and isolation to home with the mother. She subsequently became a model.

3) A 4-year-old preschool boy was referred by the schools for fire setting, strangling his mother's poodle to death, and attacking his mother with a knife. Grandparents initially won him over. Imagery through art therapy uncovered an interest in mechanical design, which led to referral to involvement at a large tool-and-die design facility with excellent results.

4) A 3-year, 10-month-old nursery school boy was referred for being disruptive and totally unmanageable. After two visits he was being tutored in geometry, and mother's untapped genius led to her enrollment at a local university.

5) A 16-year-old male with an IQ of 180 was treated in traditional one-to-one therapy with hospitalization, and family therapy for aggressive behavior with teachers and peers, and severe depression. Though the parents were above-average professionals, work essentially centered around stabilizing family interaction. On leave from the hospital, following an enormous intellectual battle with his parents over desire for enrollment in college courses, the patient committed suicide with cyanide. I believe this was a tragic loss of a potentially highly creative individual.

One recurring selection factor, on retrospect, seemed to be presence of a profound degree of nascent energy. How many infants and toddlers possess it? How many of us still posses it? Primary and secondary narcissism, so long denigrated, may not be entirely virtue-less after all.

Potential for creativity
develops as a
continuous process of
resynthesis. Our unconscious
adds to each day's efforts
and adds to our
total being.

Chapter 7
A Resynthesis of the Creative Being
as a Participant in Evolution

My intent has been to study and develop the concept of the creative being as an entity distinct from the masses, any particular social group, or professional discipline. It is almost a necessity that the creative being strives to remain apart from these organizations. Anthropology and sociology will continue trying to understand the way civilizations and societies emerge and evolve. Here, we explore the how, why, and what of the initiators of the evolving process that civilizations and societies incorporate.

The most difficult task confronting the creative being is maintaining fluidity in the face of constant pressure for stabilization from the world of humans. The capacity for fluidity is the essence of the creative being. A simultaneous requirement is the capacity for concretization: to bring original thought into established fact. The nidus of these criteria appears in the schizophrenic's loose associations and concreteness without the ability to hold it all together.

We must use a basic philosophical and theoretical framework to make sense of the day-to-day direction and perspective of the creative soul. Our dream life from the previous night opens doors to the important feelings from the previous day as well as these arising from the new day. Creativity develops from a continuous process of resynthesis: our unconscious adds to each day's efforts and Our total being.

There is nothing magical about creativity. Rather, it is a matter of being in tune with the more simple laws of the universe and our soul, individual and collective. Enormous energy, heart, and perseverance are required to enter into the realm of the creative being. One cannot do the actual work for another; one can only attempt to touch the spirit in others and wish them well.

In 1962 Indiana University press published Margharita Laski's now classic work, *Ecstasy: A Study of Some Secular and Religious Experiences.* Laski outlined a six-step process underlying Eureka! breakthroughs, those creative insights, revelations, and transformations of the mind that change the history of science, philosophy, art, or religion. Pearce, in *Biology of Transcendence*, gives examples including: mathematician William Hamilton's translation of a symbolic flash of lightning into the cornerstone of modern math, August Kekule's perception of a snake with its tail in its mouth, an ancient symbol forming a peculiar configuration. After translating his vision, he gave science the theory of the benzene ring, cornerstone of modern chemistry. Gordon Gould, an optical physicist, had a sudden vision of a symbolic structure of enormous complexity and detail, which etched itself into his brain indelibly. After a weekend of writing the essence and remarkable implications of what he had visualized, he had roughed out the theory of laser light, for which he would eventually receive the Nobel Prize in physics.

The six steps in Laski's creative discovery process are:

1. Asking the question. A suggestion, idea, or intuitive hunch, something we long to find out about, an enigma we want to solve. A quest must become not just the focus of our life, but such a passionate intensity that we are seized by it. Until we are seized in the pursuit of our notion by that which we think we have seized, the level of passion will not be sufficient to ignite our movement toward Eureka.

2. Searching for the answer. We must explore all avenues that might be useful in our search. Laski points out that we must leave no stone unturned gathering the materials for our answer. The early stages are generally exciting, colored as they are by the conviction that the answer is always just around the corner.

3. Hitting the plateau period. A time of stagnation inevitably arrives when no more materials can be found, no more discipline can be harnessed, and no more sacrifices can be made. Frustration, despair, even bitterness and disillusionment occur. Yet this is a time of gestation, that part of creation that lies beyond our doing and can't be engineered. We might go through several plateaus before the answer forms and breaks through to us. And the breakthrough may never come at all.

4. Giving up all hope. No dawn follows the dark; all possibilities are exhausted. We have tried everything but no answer is found. We feel we have wasted our life to no avail and we quit

5. Breaking through. Real quitting clears the circuitry of mind, brain, and body and makes room for the answer to appear. It has access to us—at which point the answer arrives complete, when least expected in a single instant's insight.

6. Translating the answer. This is the critical step, the one in which far more revelations perish than survive to see the light of day. Our instant, breakthrough insight can't be communicated as given. It must be translated into language that allows it to be shaped with others of a like mind. Until this is done, it hangs in limbo, halfway between creation and created until it is properly birthed into the world. (Now, perhaps, the reader may be able to understand why this work has taken more than 40 years).

Creativity is an existential
diffusion into a
contemporary universal
contradiction
arising from the process
of evolution. Its result is
a resynthesis
and expansion of
evolution.

Chapter 8
Creativity as Contemporary Existential Process

Creativity can be viewed as an existential diffusion into a contemporary universal contradiction arising from the process of evolution. Its result is a resynthesis and expansion of evolution. Only the spiritual being has the ability to be in tune with the universe. The soul contains the prerequisites for this work. Freud, Hartman, Erikson, and Rappaport are 20th century creative beings in the field of psychoanalytical psychology. Certainly there are many examples in other creative fields.

The evolutionary process—which can be viewed as a structure of the personality—consists of many existential moments. This evolution is particularly true when we focus on the growth process.

The objective of this work on resynthesis of the creative being refines the process of creativity so it will be more efficient for those entering this arena. Aspiring individuals can take heart that one can direct the self with hope for success, rather than be discouraged about having little control over one's creativity.

Many human beings often stumble upon creativity, while others appreciate it from the beginning of their sojourn. The creative being needs to find and develop a medium to enhance his/her personal process of diffusion into the energy of the universe. Most creative people suffer some kind of agony or pain to move themselves into a creative mood. To capture existential moments of universal contradiction and diffuse rapidly into them creatively is the essence of a creative being's existence.

One's medium, therefore, essentially must have a heavy substrate in the arena of feelings. Over time, creative beings usually discover a particular medium that is quite effective. My own medium involves playing Beethoven as a background and using the process of free association. Contradiction lies at the heart of feeling and provides a natural entry into whatever contradiction within the universe one wishes to grasp.

We often see attempts at creatively during times of devastating explosions of nature. Three major catastrophic occurrences of nature in 2005 come to mind: the tsunami of Indonesia, the U.S. tropical hurricane Katrina, and the earthquake in Pakistan. There have been similar occurrences, rarely so close to one another, however. Worldwide attention and involvement have generated great existential energy that might have translated into a significant effect on the processes of evolution.

Scientists immediately sprang into action to enhance their study and understanding of these phenomena. What will be the impact of people and society on the further evolution of the universe as a result of these three phenomena?

Here, political forces repeatedly took over initial global responses and essentially repressed the potential for creative actions. Unfortunately, no creative leader arose akin to Martin Luther King, Mahatma Ghandi, Nelson Mandela, or Caesar Chavez. These individuals' ability to relinquish the self to a movement within a societal group has effected a major affectual evolutionary change within millions of people.

It is too early to know whether physicists and other scientists develop the means to study the correlation of these catastrophes and, perhaps, make such events predictable and/or preventable in the future.

Dr. Jerome Schulte

The ultimate challenge
of science is to
unlock knowledge
and understanding
of the essence of
the universe.

Chapter 9
Emergence and Biological Transcendence
A New Approach to the Dilemma of
Creationism versus Evolution

The Dover, Penn., school board court decision highlights the ongoing dilemma of Creationism versus Evolution. The entire energy of the universe is based on and dependent on contradiction—as basic as the positive and negative poles of the magnet or positive and negative ions in chemistry. The contradiction in theories, regarding the universe's origin, becomes almost whimsical. It is there; it must be there; it has always been there; and it always will be there.

I developed my thesis of personality development using the metaphor of two opposite sides of a coin having equal contributions to the value, because both theories contribute to an ultimate understanding of the universe. The challenge has been finding a medium that helps understand essence of the universe.

The developing philosophy of emergence and the scientific development of transcendence follow a pattern of "being able to rise and go beyond at ever-higher levels of complexity" (Pearce[48], which evolved from *A Crack in the Cosmic Egg* to *The Biology Of Transcendence.* They evolved, in large measure as a result of advances in neurocardiology and neurobrain scientific knowledge.

Could the unexplained architectural remains in the Baalbek mountains of Lebanon, the ruins of Manchu Picchu in Peru, and the burial mounds of North America be steps of those civilizations transcending to a greater knowledge and understanding of the cosmos? The rest of humankind evolved through increased scientific knowledge to a philosophy of emergence.

Emergence theorists agree that nature's complex structures—from proteins to cells to brains—are more than simple combinations of their parts. They "emerged" from lower to higher levels of reality. This means each level of reality is in some way "richer" than what came before. (Think of the metamorphosis of the butterfly from fertilized egg to caterpillar to chrysalis to emergence of the wrinkled wing adult butterfly).

It is interesting that science is testing causal closure, that physical events only have physical causes. Consciousness might have irreducible causal capacities. That it demands scientific study is a major breakthrough, as a result of emergence philosophy.

The essence of the universe is energy. Scientists are now able to study the energy emanating from the heart and the way it is holistically nested within the energy of the planet, solar system, and the universe. In his work, Pearce also describes in his work that science now allows us to study the neural connections of the heart to the brain and the influence of the heart on brain functions. Within this mutually interdependent heart brain system, the intelligence of our heart and the intellect in our head should each influence and give rise to and embellish the other. Gradually, the scientific foundation is being laid that has underscored my life's work: "First You Feel; Then You Know."

I have been influenced from a spiritual standpoint by early Aramaic scholars' conception that the home of the Creator and the Created is all one Cosmos. With the concepts of sin and hell, religions have complicated the perspective of unity by creating a sense of separateness. The unifying principle of a one-cosmos position is best demonstrated in the Lord's Prayer, "Thy kingdom come. Thy will be done. On earth as it is in heaven." Aramaic was the predominant language in the area where

Jesus lived during his human experience, and the original language more beautifully describes this unity of Creator and created..

It would have been necessary the Creator experience "feelings" to begin the creative process. From the Created's position, as described by Pearce, the intrinsic need for growth, experienced through feelings, drives the evolutionary force of the universe.

The concepts I have conveyed throughout this book are most closely embodied in the foundations of transcendence biology and philosophy, on the periphery of emergence philosophy. My guiding principle goes beyond current transcendence positions. Affects (feelings) propel the physical, chemical, biological, and spiritual process of transcendence. Humans connect with other human beings, domesticated pets, and a divine being through feelings. The meeting point for creative design and evolution is very simply the feeling of love.

Perhaps humans can learn that the contradiction with which they have always struggled is domination (war) versus love. The arena in which this contradiction has been fought throughout history is law. For Christians, it began with the ten Commandments, which at that time needed to be quite harsh, negative, and forceful. Fortunately, when human beings, including the religious, are quizzed regarding the greatest commandment of all, they respond: "Love Thy Neighbor As Thyself."

I Corinthians 13:13

Finding and
developing one's
cosmological identity
is the challenge
of all 21st
century beings.

Chapter 10
Nanotechnology, Singularity, Metaphysics and Cosmology

As a final step, on becoming a creative being, realizing the ultimate need in humans and the universe for ever continuing growth, requires one to grasp and incorporate their contemporary inherent processes of growth.

Nanotechnology is a miniaturization process that can perform complex tasks on a near molecular level: one millionth of a meter in size. Human biological transcendence—as discussed in the previous chapter referring to Pearce's *The Biology of Transcendence*—led to the current evolutionary development of nanotechnology. Although its origins can be traced back more than 50 years, nanotechnology gained impetus in 1985 with the discovery of the bucky ball by Smalley and colleagues.[50,51]

Practical applications on the human biological level are computerized. There are already numerous FDA-approved therapeutics, including neural implants. One application has been approved to repair and replace biological neurons destroyed by Parkinson's disease. I n *The Singularity Is Near,*[49] Kurzweil beautifully illustrates the law of accelerating returns: the inherent acceleration of the rate of evolution with technological evolution as a continuation of biological evolution. As Kurzweil, points out: human progress is exponential (expanding by repeatedly multiplying by a constant) rather than linear (expanding by repeatedly adding a constant).

Human progress is seductive. It begins slowly, but at a critical point it becomes explosive and profoundly transformative. Evolution creates patterns of increasing order. Evolutionary processes work through indirection. Evolution creates a capability and uses that capability to evolve the next stage. Accelerating returns is why the next stage goes more quickly and the fruits of an evolutionary process grow exponentially. Biological evolution and human technology show continued acceleration.

Most advanced mammals have added one cubic inch of brain matter every thousand years. Research in 2006 documents brain growth rate is progressively accelerating and measurable. In the technological arena, we are roughly doubling the computational capability of computers every year, while simultaneously seeing an acceleration of the rate of miniaturization of these computers. They, in turn, accelerate brain growth.

We now have a need to study metaphysics as the philosophy that tries to explain reality and knowledge and studies the nature of things. Metaphysics includes 3 arenas.

Epistemology: The Theory of Knowledge

Ontology: Study of the Nature of Reality

Cosmology: Theory of the origin of the Universe and its laws as a whole in space and time: what it is now, what was it in the past, and what it is likely to be in the future.

Buckminster Fuller was our 20th century Leonardo Da Vinci. His genius as a philosopher, systems engineer, inventor, designer, author and futurist continues to have an impact, beyond his death even to this day, on humanity and our evolution.

A "Fuller Picture" by L.Steven Seiden carries Buckminster Fuller's assertion that the sense of separation from nature is a dangerous illusion resulting from reductionism and over specialization. Humanities evolutionary success is dependent on our willingness to learn from the emergent behavior of the whole system. This led him to the question how we envision the context of our existence reimagining a big picture in which our species is situated within the whole continuum of creation.

In "Operating Manual for Spaceship Earth" Fuller asks: "Can we think of adequately and incisively, what we mean by universe, For universe is, inferentially, the biggest system. If we could start with universe, we would automatically avoid leaving out any strategically critical variables.

We find no record as yet of man having successfully defined the universe scientifically and comprehensibly, including the non simultaneous and only partially overlapping, micro-macro, always and everywhere transforming, physical and metaphysical omni-complimentary but non-identical events.

Fuller redefined " Universe" {eventually differentiating it through capitalization snd dropping the definite article "the"} to include both the specialized insights of science and our metaphysical capacities and experiences. Yet he insisted the Universe is far more than simply mind plus matter, contending that the whole is always more than the sum of the individual parts. He summarized the perspective with the pithy generalization U=MP, proposing that Universe is the synergistic result of the metaphysical multiplied by the physical (Synergistics 162.0). He called his work "Comprehensive Anticipatory Design Science", by which he took it upon himself to attempt to solve some of the greatest challenges he predicted would soon be facing humanity.

In the 21st century, this synergistic systems oriented approaches are more critical than ever.

The Buckminster Fuller Institute has formed a global network of design science practitioners actively applying these principles in their own work and to address Fuller's challenge to " make the world work for 100% of humanity in the shortest possible time through spontaneous co-operation without ecological offense or disadvantage of anyone, The Buckminster Fuller Institute Challenge thru.'Metropolis Magazine: provides a Socially-Responsible Designers Highest Award for a regionally specific, yet globally applicable, comprehensive anticipatory integrated approach to solving human beings and the worlds most complex problems.

In his initial aspiration of starting with Universe Fuller eliminated the often-used motivation that so many of us begin with-making money or making a living for ourselves and families (recall from Section I Chapter 6 "Success Neurosis"). From that narrow context, a person often misses the opportunity to really make a difference and succeed well beyond what she initially imagined. The shift in perspective can be seen in Bucky's famous statement "You can make money or you can make sense, the two are mutually exclusive".

Metaphysics, has to date in history, failed to keep up its required role in the area of epistemology, or the study of knowledge necessary to the advancement of Universe and humanity. Artificial Intelligence (AI) will also fail to fully provide what will be needed in this arena. Section I ' The Affectual Universe" encapsulated my life-long quotation to my clients " First You Feel- Then You Know" .Only knowledge and understanding of human emotions can fill in that gap heretofore missing in epistemology.

Section II The Physical Universe highlighted the metaphysical realm of ontology-again only fully knowledgeable thru the arena of human feelings by its incorporation of the universe.

Section III The Spiritual Universe clearly advances the role of human emotions in the development of the mutually shared Creator-Created Universe The new scientific data on the heart as the primary route of information from the cosmos to the brain dramatically opens a new world to study Universe.

Although there's a certain amount of plasticity, we have a hundred trillion neural connections in our brains. Biological intelligence is essentially fixed; however, neurological intelligence is growing exponentially. The crossover point will be in the 2020s when the non-biological portion of our civilization will predominate. But it will still be an expression of human civilization.

Every time we have technological gains, we make gains in life expectancy. Singularity will represent, as Kurzweil states, "the culmination of the merger of our biological thinking and existence with our technology, resulting in a world that is still human but transcends our biological roots. What will remain unequivocally human is: ours is the species that inherently seeks to extend its physical and mental reach beyond current limitations."

Following the development of nanotechnology, we see a similar explosive evolutionary development in artificial intelligence (AI). AI will surpass human intelligence in the near future. AI will continue to improve itself through its own self-generated programs, as opposed to improving via human intelligent design, which has been the case in its origin and development. I find myself posing a series of questions in the light of these explosive ongoing evolutionary developments: Will this explosion of knowledge mean coming to an ultimate understanding of human intelligence, knowledge, and human consciousness? Will this development lead to a change in the spiritual component of humanness? Will human beings be able to construct and live in their own virtual reality and potentially be able to extend life and prevent death?

If some evil force controlled this artificial intelligence, would it require some form of universal totalitarianism to ensure human safety from the destructive use of this power? Can limits be established on the dissemination of the destructive elements of artificial intelligence? These questions probe the inner workings of the human mind and its ability to expand beyond the human being.

It would do well at this point to review the first three philosophical theorems of this book:

The essence of humanness is need.

The essence of need is feelings.

The essence of feelings is growth.

My summation for the essence of humanness, therefore, is the need for continued growth through feelings. First you feel; then you know. Two sides of the coin illustrate the complementary contradictory forces engendered by every need. Now, however, it becomes necessary to add the third dimension. The width of the coin expresses the intrinsic value of the coin, as well as our humanness, through the processes of contradiction and fulfillment, in each growth step.

Now let us return to the issue of consciousness, which I prefer to term humanness. We have a distinct individuality as humans that cannot be instantly merged with others. Our consciousness is ultimately a subjective experience, and is unmeasurable by fully objective means. Objective measurement is incompatible with the very concept of subjective experience. That realization led to my five arenas of feelings as an attempt to approximate a measurement to consciousness.

Finally, we need to study how cosmology contributes to consciousness. Cosmology is the study of the general nature of the universe, as a whole in space and time: what is it now, what was it in the past, and what is it likely to be in the future. This philosophy combines scientific knowledge and speculative metaphysics. One major scientific fact recently established is that the universe is expanding at an ever-increasing rate, similar to biological and technological explosive acceleration. As cosmologists Joel Primack[21] and his wife Nancy Ellen Abrams write in *The View from the Center of the Universe,* "There is no deeper source of meaning for human beings than to experience our own lives as reflecting the nature and origin of the universe. We may be participants in a great cosmic story as far beyond our imagination as that which atoms and cells are playing for us." However, the couple limit us to objective measurements, utilizing our physical and brain size as determinants, to our ability to know.

Primack is a physicist; in contrast Abrams is a philosopher, writer, and musician. On Fridays Nancy still lights candles and prays in the ancient tradition of Jewish women, and has a CD track The Handwriting Of God about the cosmic background and radiation from the Big Bang. As to the question of do they believe in God? They believe in God as nothing less than the process of opening our personal lines of contact with the unknown potential of the universe. I can't help but wonder if they would be willing to agree their "personal lines of contact" might involve their subjective feelings as human beings and have validity equal to the objective measurements of physics?

Primack and Abrams make a valid point. However, we need to realize and accept the importance of our cosmic identity and the impact we have on the future of our cosmos and descendants. Our vital importance at this time, unequaled by any other time in cosmological history, is setting trends in motion that will very likely experience exponential expansion. Their effect on the universe cannot be underestimated or dismissed. We must bring together the major processes: biological transcendence, nanotechnology, singularity, and cosmology eternal inflation. Their shared property of exponential growth, most profoundly impacted by the exponential growth of our human population in the past two decades, will shape the meaningfulness of our lives as citizens of the universe in the 21st century.

Primack and Abrams highlight the difficulty people have grasping the vision, awareness, knowledge, and acceptance of the importance of their cosmic identity. They encourage us to use our collective metaphorical unconscious to come up with ideas or symbols that would help us identify our fore and aft cosmological connections.

This could be helpful, but process is content. If we follow the outline of my book, and it could become a part of the educational process of our youth, we would arrive at where we need to be in a relatively short time. Another avenue unconsciously used throughout history to solidify our cosmological connections has been universal communication involving emotions of youth—namely, music.

We are cocreators of our universe and participate in its evolution just as surely as we participate in our own evolution. Thus, the creator and the created give rise to each other. Creator and created as a co-inspiring dynamic make imperative a natural law intelligence, no matter how innate or genetically coded, can unfold within us only when an actual model for that intelligence is given to us. All humans or vital force must have their generative source in affectual growth.

Each person has a destiny to fulfill in becoming a cocreator of our universe and model for those that follow. Thrilling moments and ecstasy await those who undertake the processes of becoming a creative being. May your life's journey be fruitful.

Summary

The underlying principle of this book is that at the time of creation the essence of each and every human being is the need to continually grow throughout one's life and become the creative being that is within each of us. The book further brings into focus the universal truth that individuals and societies are able to grow though need fulfillment and that there is a logical sequence to this process.

Detailed insights are given from earliest childhood development all the way through adulthood. It includes the nature of societies development and the challenges that must be faced in order to fulfill it's members. The contradiction to this is death for the individual and society.

A major contradiction within all human beings and therefore within all societies arises out of the internal affective needs that define our humanness and our external needs to incorporate the universe and cosmos that define our universal being. This book details the steps individuals and societies are confronted with "to become one with oneself and one's universe". Section I is titled The Affectual Universe and Section II The Physical Universe including a never before exposition on the Criminal Personality.

Sexuality is defined as the energizing force behind the process enabling one "to become one with oneself and one's universe". It is only when there has been successful synthesis of these 2 complimentary sides of our being that we are ready to enter into true creativity and spirituality.

Along this path of human development there are many potential pitfalls many can and often do experience. The book identifies the common enabling and disabling causes of most individual and societal dysfunction. It details in a step by step manner how the dysfunctions come about and lays down a blueprint for the prevention or later resolution of the dysfunctions.

As of this century we must deal with the emerging world society. What must be clearly understood is that society must be guided by the principle to provide freedom for each and every individual to be and to grow as driven by the essence of their soul. The amazing document, The Declaration of Independence, clearly states it is the inalienable right of the individual to have freedom and the right to the pursuit of happiness which can only occur through the fulfillment of one's essence.

The caption on the first page of "The Fountainhead" by Ayn Rand portrays these principles and will forever be a classic. "Whatever their future, at the dawn of their lives, men seek a noble vision of man's future and of life's potential."

In closing a final emphasis is given to the fact that societies and now The World Society can only emerge in a positive fashion as the freedom of the individual for self determination underlies it's laws.

Immortality, likewise, is dependent on this freedom of self-determination of the individual reaching one's ultimate fruition and fulfillment.

And now faith, hope and love
abide, these three;
and the greatest of these
is love

I Corinthians 13:13

BIBLIOGRAPHY

1. Franz, Norm. *Money and Wealth in the New Millennium: Prophetic Guide to the End Time Transfer of Wealth.* Denver, CO: Whitestone Press, March 3, 2001.

2. Universal Declaration of Human Rights Article 26, Section 2. Google.com search for universal declaration of human rights.

3. Erikson, Erich H. *Eight Ages of Man in Childhood and Society.* 2nd Ed. New York:
   W.W. Norton, 1963.

4. Schulte, Jerome L. "Study and Treatment of 46 Psychotic Patients with Convictions of Homicide." *American Journal of Forensic Psychiatry* 8:3 (1987): 47-54.

5. Schulte, Jerome L. "Long-Term Treatment of a Psychotic Sociopathic Homicidal Patient: Case Study." *American Journal of Forensic Psychiatry* 3 (1989): 59-72.

6. Coleman, James William. *The Criminal Elite: Understanding White-Collar Crime.* 4th Ed. New York: St. Martin's Press, 1998.

7. Konase, Irving M., Copi Late, Carl Cohen, & Kenneth McMahon. *Introduction to Logic.* 14th Ed., Pearson Prentice Hall, New York, October, 2010..

8. Besant, Annie Wood, and Leadbeater, Charles W. *Thought-Forms.* Wheaton, Illinois: Theosophical Publishing House, 1967.

9. Erikson, Erich H. *Identity, Youth and Crisis.* New York: W.W. Norton, 1969.
   Folsing, Albrecht. *Albert Einstein: A Biography.* Trans. Ewald Oser. New York: Viking Press, 1997.

10. Plato. *The Republic.* 1992. Trans. G.M.A. Grube. New York: Hackett, 1992.

11. US Supreme Court Decision Death Penalty for Minors. Roper v Simmons; March 1, 2005 Docket #03-633.

12. LeBoyer, Frederich. *Birth Without Violence.* First American Ed. New York: Knopf/Random House, 1976.

13. Fromm, Erich. *The Art of Loving.* New York: Harper, 1956.

14. Ariew, Roger, and Watkins, Eric. *Readings in Modern Philosophy 1: Descartes, Spinoza, Leibnitz.* New York: Hackett, 2002.

15. Spitz, Rene A. [with W. Godfrey Cobliner]. *The First Year of Life. A Psychoanalytic Study of Normal and Deviant Development of Object Relations.* New York: International Universities Press, 1965.

16. Michener, James A. *Centennial.* New York: Random House, 1974.

17. Frank, Philipp. *Einstein: His Life And Times.* Trans. George Rosin. New York: De Capo Press, 1947.

18. Salmon, Merrilee. *Introduction to Logic and Critical Thinking.* New York: Wadsworth, 2005.

19. Kopp, Josef V. *Teilhard DeChardin: A New Synthesis of Evolution.* Glen Rock, New Jersey: Paulist Press, 1964.

20. Sheehy, Gail. *Passages. Predictable Crises of Adult Life.* New York: E.P. Dutton, 1976.

21. Primack, Joel R, and Adams, Nancy Ellen. *The View from the Center of the Universe.* New York: Riverhead Books Penguin Group, 2006.

22. Beiser, Frederick C. *The Cambridge Companion to Hegel.* New York: Cambridge University Press, 1993.

23. Rado, Sandor. *Adaptational Psychodynamics: Motivation and Control.* Ed. Jason Aronson. New York: New York Science House, 1969.

24. Nietszche, Frednich. *Beyond Good and Evil: Prelude to a Philosophy of the Future.* Trans. Walter Kaufman. New York: Random House, 1968.

25. Lungren, John C. *Healing Richard Nixon. A Doctor's Memoir.* Lexington, KY: University Press of Kentucky, 2003.

26. Nixon, Richard M. *The Memoirs of Richard Nixon.* New York: Grosset and Dunlap, 1978.

27. Baker, Marilyn with Sally Brompton. *Exclusive! The Inside Story of Patricia Hearst and The S. L. A.* New York: McMillan, 1974.

28. Bartlett, Donald, and. Steele-Empire, James B. *The Life, Legend and Madness of Howard Hughes.* New York: Broadway Books, 1979.

29. Pearce, Joseph Chilton and Hartmann, Thom. *The Crack in the Cosmic Egg: New Constructs of Mind and Reality.* Rochester, VT: Park Street Press, 2002.

30. Whitehead, Alfred North. *Process and Reality: An Essay in Cosmology.* New York: Free Press, 1978.

31. Blake, William. *The Complete Poetry and Prose of William Blake.* Ed. David V. Erdman. New York: Anchor Books, 1982.

32. Dostoyevsky, Fyodor. *Crime and Punishment.* Trans. David McDuff. New York: Viking, 1991.

33. Steele, Brandt F. *Working with Abusive Parents from a Psychiatric Point of View.* US Department of Health, Education & Welfare. Washington, DC: US Government Printing Office, 1976.

34. Kemp, Henry C. *Child Abuse.* Cambridge, MA: Harvard University Press, 1978.

35. Janov, Arthur. *Biology of Love*. Amherst, New York: Brometheus Books, 2000.

36. Niven, David "Young Prodigies Take Off Under Special Program." *Smithsonian.* October 1977: 76-82.

37. Castaneda, Carlos. *The Second Ring of Power.* New York: Simon & Schuster, 1977.

38. Castaneda, Carlos. *Tales of Power.* New York: Simon & Schuster, 1971.

39. Leadbeater, CW. *A Textbook of Theosophy*. India: The Theosophical Publishing House, 1912.

40. Schwarz, Ted. *The Hillside Strangler. A Murderer's Mind.* 1st Ed. Garden City, NY: Doubleday, 1981.

41. Trevor-Roper, Hugh R. *The Last Days of Hitler*. 4th Ed. New York: MacMillian, 1971.

42. Keys, Daniel. *The Minds of Billy Milligan.* 1st Ed. New York: Random House, 1981.

43. *A Harry Stack Sullivan Case Seminar. Treatment of a Young Male Schizophrenic.* 1st Ed. Eds. Robert G. Kvarnes and Gloria H. Parloff. New York: W.W. Norton, 1976.

44. William Alanson White Association. *The Contributions of Harry Stack Sullivan: A Symposium on Interpol Theory in Psychiatry and Social Science.* 1st Ed. Ed. Patrick Mullahy. New York: Hermitage House, 1952.

45. Arieti, Silvano. *American Handbook of Psychiatry.* 2nd Ed. New York: Basic Books, 1974.

46. Polanski, Roman. *Roman Polanski Interviews.* Ed. Paul Cronin. Jackson, MS: University Press of Mississippi, 2005.

47. Lindsay, Hal, et al. *The Late Great Planet Earth.* Grand Rapids, MI: Zondervan Publishing House, 1977.

48. Chilton. Pearce Joseph. *The Biology of Transcendence: A Blueprint of the Human Spirit.* Rochester, VT: Park Street Press, 2002.

49. Kurzweil, Ray. *The Singularity Is Near.* New York: Viking Penguin Press, 2005.

50. Kroto, HW, Heath, JR, O'Brien, SC, Carl, RF, and Smalley, Richard E. Nature (November 14, 1985): 162, 318.

51. Smalley, Richard E. *Discovering the Fullerenes.* Rev. Mod Phys. Vol. 69, Issue 3: 723-730: July 1997

52. Schore, Allan N. *Affect Regulation and the Origin of the Self: The Neurobiology of Emotional Development.* New York: Lawrence Erlbaum Associates, 1994.

54. Piaget, Jean. *Intelligence and Affectivity: Their Relationship During Child Development.* Palo Alto, CA Annual Reviews, Inc. 1981.

55. Piaget, Jean. *The Childs Conception of the World.* New York, Humanities Press, 1951.

56. Alexander, CN and Langer, EJ *Higher Stages of Human Development: Adult Growth Beyond Formal Operations.* Oxford Universal Press, 1988.

57. Jung, Carl G. *Man and His Symbols.* Aldus Books Limited, London, 1964

"Unconditional Love"

A priceless photo of Dr. Schulte and his greatgrandson Austin
at age 1 month, November 9, 2011.

About the Author

This book is a synthesis of his over 50 year multidimensional career in clinical and administrative psychiatry in community, military, education, state and federal mental health programs. Adolescence, juvenile, adult correctional and forensic court work have been areas of expertise. Multiple publications in The American Journal of Forensic Psychiatry correlated his work as Director of Medical Education and Recruitment at Atascadero State Hospital (the world's largest forensic hospital). Private practice in 3 states over 43 years encompassing childhood to centurion age groups. Certified expert witness in over 40 Superior and Federal Courts in California, Co-Director with Seymour Pollack M.D., Bruce Gross Director of USC Department of Psychiatry & Law and staff of a certificate program for 100 professional staff at Atascadero Hospital. Recruited staff of 40 Board Certified psychiatrists achieving highest APA Hospital Accreditation. Staff psychiatrist for substance abuse and psychotic homicidal patient treatment programs. Board of Directors San Felipe Humanitarian Alliance for 30 years.